# HOW TO ENTERTAIN WITH YOUR POCKET CALCULATOR

OLEG D. JEFIMENKO
West Virginia University

# How To Entertain With Your Pocket Calculator

Pastimes, Diversions, Games
and
Magic Tricks

With Illustrations by
David K. Walker
Waynesburg College

Electret Scientific Company
Star City

P.O. Box No. 4132
Star City, West Virginia 26505



Library of Congress Catalog Card Number 74 - 84864

Printed in the United States of America

To my wife
Valentina

# PREFACE

A remarkable property of the electronic pocket calculator that makes it uniquely suitable for entertaining in a spectacular and yet intimate manner is its innate ability to make a simultaneous visual and psychological impact upon the person operating its keyboard. This property of the calculator allows one to use it for a variety of entertainments in a manner not unlike that in which a musical instrument is used and with an analogous effect. Just as a musical instrument is capable of producing a pleasing, exciting, and moving combination of sounds, the calculator is capable of producing a delightful, exciting, and thought-provoking combination of numbers; not the abstract, lifeless numbers of yesteryear, but the brilliant, everchanging, living numbers materializing themselves with a dramatic reality in the display of the calculator.

Recreations with numbers, or mathematical entertainments, have been known since antiquity. But only now, with the advent of the pocket calculator, can they be truly enjoyed by everybody. The pocket calculator has eliminated the need for extraordinary mathematical ability which in the past was frequently required for conducting such entertainments or for participating in them. The calculator allows everybody to perform all kinds of numerical operations with unprecedented ease and speed. As a result, for the first time in history, various mathematical entertainments can now be presented in their most pure, most beautiful, and most dramatic form. No longer need they be diluted or impeded by the usually irrelevant, frequently dull, and inevitably time-consuming intermediate calculations. Moreover, with its psychological and visual impact, the calculator adds an entirely new dimension to such entertainments, transforming them into some of the most refined, stimulating, gratifying, inspiring, enjoyable, and spectacular entertainments ever devised. These were the considerations that prompted me to write this book.

In writing the book, I made use of many old mathematical recreations, diversions, tricks, and pastimes, which I "transcribed" for the pocket calculator. I also devised some new ones. In doing so, I emphasized the entertainment aspect, rather than the mathematical aspect, of the material used. Readers interested in mathematical details are advised to consult the works listed in the bibliography section at the end of the book.

The entertainments described in the book can be performed with a pocket calculator of any type, although a calculator with an 8-digit display and a floating decimal point is assumed throughout the book. Some of the entertainments may require slight, and usually self-evident, modifications if calculators of other types are used.

The readers wishing to present a more or less formal "entertainment program" should plan it carefully. The various entertainments comprising such a program should be presented in the order of increasing complexity and sophistication. The time allocated to each of them should not be uncomfortably short. It is advisable to write down beforehand a concise outline of the program to be presented. The sheet of paper on which such an outline is written can also be used for "free-hand" calculations that must be done in the course of the entertainments. To simplify the preparations of such programs I have supplemented most of the entertainments described in the book by "calculation formulas" that show in a condensed form the essential calculations involved in a particular entertainment. A typical program outline utilizing such formulas is presented in the Appendix. It starts with simple diversions taken from Chapters 1, 2, and 3, makes use of the progressively more spectacular tricks taken from Chapters 6, 7, and 8, and ends with a humorous trick taken from Chapter 9.

Although the book is designed primarily as an entertainment guide, it can also serve as a teaching aid in elementary mathematics classes where the electronic pocket calculator is used.

The book should add some pleasant and unexpected variety to the subject matter in such classes.

I am pleased to express my gratitude to my wife Valentina for helping me to test the various entertainments included in the book, for typing the manuscript, and for otherwise assisting me with writing and making the book ready for publication. I am also pleased to express my gratitude to Dr. D. K. Walker for reading the manuscript, for discussing it with me, and for adorning the book with excellent illustrations.

October 1974 Oleg D. Jefimenko

# CONTENTS

# HOW TO ENTERTAIN
# WITH YOUR
# POCKET CALCULATOR

# 1

# MINI-TRICKS AND KEYBOARD PUZZLES

Many captivating arithmetical pastimes can be enjoyed by anyone having a pocket calculator. In this chapter we describe a number of such pastimes, presented in the form of elementary tricks, puzzles, and problems, that can be used for entertaining a single person as well as several persons at a small party or a friendly get-together.

These pastimes are also very well suited for teaching your friends or your family how to use the calculator. Most of the "sophisticated" tricks and entertainments described in the subsequent chapters require that your friends perform by themselves certain operations on your calculator. The pastimes described here will help them to get acquainted with your calculator in a pleasant and rewarding way.

Solutions to the problems and puzzles

presented in this chapter are given at the end of the chapter.

## 1-1. THE STRETCHING OPERATION

Ask your friend to enumerate the various arithmetical operations known to him (subtraction, multiplication, etc.). Then tell him that he has left out the "stretching" operation. Since no such operation really exists (we invented it for the purpose of this trick), your friend will probably insist that there is no such thing. Pass your calculator to him and ask him to enter in the display some one-digit number. Then ask him to multiply it by 11, 111, 1111, and so forth. The results will be multidigit numbers built up from the original one-digit number repeated as many times as there are 1's in the number by which the original number is multiplied. You can declare to your friend that these numbers represent his original number stretched twice, thrice, four times, etc., its original length, and that a multiplication producing such "stretched" numbers is called the "stretching" operation.

*Example*

Let the original number be 5. The "stretching" operations produce:

$$5 \times 11 = 55 \qquad 5 \times 11111 = 55555$$
$$5 \times 111 = 555 \qquad 5 \times 111111 = 555555$$

$5 \times 1111 = 5555 \qquad 5 \times 1111111 = 5555555$

$5 \times 11111111 = 55555555$, etc.

## 1-2. THE STRETCHING-SKIPPING OPERATION

Once again ask your friend to enumerate the various arithmetical operations and then tell him that he has failed to mention the "stretching-skipping" operation (which, of course, is also a fictitious one). Pass the calculator to him and ask him to enter in the display some one-digit number. Then ask him to multiply it by 101, 10101, etc. Now declare that this multiplication is called the "stretching-skipping" operation because it "leaves empty spaces as it stretches the original number."

*Example*

Let your friend enter 6 in the calculator. The "stretching-skipping" operations produce:

$$6 \times 101 = 606$$
$$6 \times 10101 = 60606$$
$$6 \times 1010101 = 6060606$$
$$6 \times 101010101 = 606060606$$

$$6 \times 1001 = 6006$$
$$6 \times 101101 = 606606$$
$$6 \times 110011 = 660066$$
$$6 \times 1001001 = 6006006$$
$$6 \times 1011101 = 6066606, \text{ etc.}$$

## 1-3. THE UNIVERSAL STRETCHING AND STRETCHING-SKIPPING OPERATIONS

You can further surprise your friend by demonstrating to him "universal stretching and stretching-skipping" operations (to be sure, fictitious, as before) that can be performed upon multidigit numbers in accordance with the example shown below. An interesting application of these operations is to "stretch" or to "stretch-skip" a one-digit number into a multidigit number in several steps by using a series of appropriate "stretching" or "stretching-skipping" operations.

*Example*

*a.* "Stretching" two-, three-, and four-digit numbers:

$$34 \times 101 = 3434$$
$$34 \times 10101 = 343434$$
$$34 \times 1010101 = 34343434$$
$$345 \times 1001 = 345345$$
$$3456 \times 10001 = 34563456$$

*b.* "Stretching-skipping" two- and three-digit numbers:

$$34 \times 1001 = 34034$$
$$34 \times 10001 = 340034$$
$$34 \times 100001 = 3400034$$
$$34 \times 1001001 = 34034034$$
$$345 \times 10001 = 3450345$$

*FIGURE 1*

*The building blocks of these number pyramids are the digit 1. Does it mean that the foundations of these pyramids, the numbers 121, 12321, 1234321, and 123454321, can be made up from numbers containing only the digit 1?*

*c.* Repeated "stretching" of a one-digit number:

$$3 \times 11 = 33$$
$$3 \times 11 \times 101 = 3333$$
$$3 \times 11 \times 10101 = 333333$$
$$3 \times 111 \times 1001 = 333333$$
$$3 \times 11 \times 1010101 = 33333333$$
$$3 \times 1111 \times 10001 = 33333333$$

## 1-4. THE FOUR PYRAMIDS

Here is a nice puzzle for you and your friends. The four "number pyramids" shown in Fig. 1 have one property in common: their building blocks are the digit 1. Does it mean that the foundations of these pyramids, the numbers 121, 12321, 1234321, and 123454321, can be made up from numbers containing only the digit 1? See if you can obtain these four foundation numbers in the display of your calculator by pressing no number keys other than 1 and pressing it not more than four, six, eight, and ten times for the 1st, 2nd, 3rd, and 4th pyramid, respectively.

## 1-5. THE FLIP-FLOP NUMBERS

Ask your friend what kind of numbers, such as odd, even, whole, etc., he knows. Then tell him that he has left out the "flip-flop" numbers. Since no such numbers really exist (we invented the name for the purpose of this trick), he will most likely say that there is no such thing. To show him these numbers and how they "flip" and "flop," pass your calculator to him and ask him to enter in it one of the numbers given below. Then say: "Multiply this number by its last digit and divide by the first digit. The number will flip: all its digits will appear in the display of the calculator in their reverse order. Now multiply this flipped number by its last digit and divide by its first digit. The number will flop back to its original form."

*Example*

Let the number be 32967. When multiplied by 7 and divided by 3, the number becomes $32967 \times 7 \div 3 = 76923$. When this number is multiplied by 3 and divided by 7, it becomes $76923 \times 3 \div 7 = 32967$.

*Numbers suitable for this trick:*

| | | | | | |
|---|---|---|---|---|---|
| 1089 | 9801 | 10989 | 98901 | 109989 | 989901 |
| 2178 | 8712 | 21978 | 87912 | 219978 | 879912 |
| 3267 | 7623 | 32967 | 76923 | 329967 | 769923 |
| 4356 | 6534 | 43956 | 65934 | 439956 | 659934 |

These numbers can be easily constructed and memorized, once you memorize the numbers 1089, 10989, and 109989. The remaining numbers are obtained from them by subtracting 1, 2, 3, etc., from each of their two last digits and adding the same figure to each of their two first digits.

The sum of the two outermost digits in all these numbers is 10, that of the next two digits is 8, the inner digits (if present) are 9's. Note also that 109..989 = 999..9 x 11, and that 10989 = 999999 ÷ 91.

## 1-6. THE SELF-MENDING NUMBERS

Ask your friend once again to tell you what different numbers he knows. Then say: "You have left out one of the most important group of numbers — the 'self-mending' numbers." Since no such numbers really exist, your friend has certainly never heard of them. To show him these numbers and how they "mend" themselves proceed as follows. On a slip of paper write any of the numbers listed below. Then tear the paper into two pieces, so that several digits of the number (as indicated below) appear on one piece and the rest appear on the other piece. Give one piece to your friend and keep the other yourself. Now say: "Observe how the number that I have torn will become mended. I shall multiply my part by itself and write down the result. You will do the same with your part, and then you will add (subtract, for the numbers in Group *b*) your product and my product. The original number will appear in the display of the calculator fully mended." (If your calculator has a memory, there is no need to write down the products, since you can enter them into the memory, add them there, and then recall the sum for examination.)

You can also do this trick with two friends, each of whom receives a part of a number taken from the numbers in Group *c*.

*Example*

Let the number be 8833. After tearing it in two, you obtain 88 and 33. Multiplication yields 88 × 88 = 7744 and 33 × 33 = 1089. Adding the two products, your friend obtains 7744 + 1089 = 8833.

*Numbers suitable for this trick:*

*a.* Multiply each part by itself and add the products

| | | | |
|---|---|---|---|
| 1233 | (12 33) | 5882353 | (588 2353) |
| 8833 | (88 33) | 94122353 | (9412 2353) |
| 10100 | (10 100) | 99009901 | (990 09901) |
| 990100 | (990 100) | 9901009901 | (99010 09901) |

*b.* Multiply each part by itself and subtract the first product from the second

| | | | |
|---|---|---|---|
| 48 | (4 8) | 140400 | (140 400) |
| 3468 | (34 68) | 190476 | (190 476) |
| 10101 | (10 101) | 216513 | (216 513) |
| 16128 | (16 128) | 300625 | (300 625) |
| 34188 | (34 188) | 334668 | (334 668) |

*c.* Multiply each part by itself twice and add the products

| | | | |
|---|---|---|---|
| 41833 | (4 18 33) | 407001 | (40 70 01) |

| | | | |
|---|---|---|---|
| 165033 | (16 50 33) | 444664 | (44 46 64) |
| 221859 | (22 18 59) | 487215 | (48 72 15) |
| 336700 | (33 67 00) | 982827 | (98 28 27) |

## 1-7. THE SAILING FLEET PUZZLE

Each ship of the sailing fleet shown in Fig. 2 carries two numbers on its hull. These numbers, in a secret code, identify the number of masts that each ship has. Using the calculator, break the code and determine how many masts are there on the ships that are not completely visible in the picture.

## 1-8. ONE, TWO, THREE . . . ONE HUNDRED

Here is an interesting keyboard problem that you can present to your friends: obtain the number 100 in the display of the calculator by pressing once each of the keys 1, 2, 3, 4, 5, 6, 7, 8, 9 and pressing at will such other keys (+, —, ÷, ×, =, 0, etc.) as may be needed to obtain the final 100. Using some of the sample calculations given below, show your friends how it can be done and then ask them to try to do it in their own way.

*Example*

*a.* Simple direct sequence

$$12 + 3 - 4 + 5 + 67 + 8 + 9 = 100$$

*FIGURE 2*

*The numbers on the hulls of these ships identify the number of masts on each ship. How many masts are there on the ships that are not completely visible in the picture?*

*b.* Simple reverse sequence

$$9 \times 8 + 7 + 6 + 5 + 4 + 3 + 2 + 1 = 100$$

*c.* Simple mixed sequence

$$2 \times 3 + 1 + 4 + 5 + 67 + 8 + 9 = 100$$

*d.* Algebraic sequence (for calculators with memory or with appropriate chain operation facility)

$$(1 + 2 - 3 - 4) \times (5 - 6 - 7 - 8 - 9) = 100$$

## 1-9. FORBIDDEN KEYS

Suppose that you are not allowed to use certain keys of your calculator. How would you go about obtaining various numbers in the display of the calculator without using the forbidden keys? There are many delightful puzzles that are based on such a restriction in operating the calculator. Here is an example: you are told to obtain 15 in the display by using no number keys other than 2. After some reflection and experimentation you find that you can do it by performing the operation $22 \div 2 + 2 + 2$. But can you and your friends do the puzzles given below? Try them and see for yourself.

1. *One.* Obtain 1 in the display by pressing several times the same number key, other than 1, and not pressing any other number

key.

2. *Two.* Obtain 2 in the display by pressing three times the same number key, other than 2, and not pressing any other number key.

3. *Three.* Obtain 3 in the display by pressing four times the same number key and not pressing any other number key. Can you do it: (a) without using the "—" key, (b) without using the "+" key?

4. *Four.* Obtain 4 in the display by pressing 3 four times and not pressing any other number key.

5. *Ten.* Obtain 10 in the display by pressing four times the same number key and not pressing any other number key.

6. *Another ten.* Obtain 10 in the display by pressing 1 three times and not pressing any other number key.

7. *And another ten.* Obtain 10 in the display by pressing 3 five times and not pressing any other number key.

8. *One more ten.* Obtain 10 in the display by pressing no number keys other than 9.

9. *Eleven.* Obtain 11 in the display by pressing no number keys other than 2.

10. *Sixteen.* Obtain 16 in the display by pressing 5 four times and not pressing any other number key.

11. *Twenty-four.* Obtain 24 in the display by pressing 2 three times and not pressing any other number key.

12. *Another twenty-four.* Obtain 24 in the

display by pressing 3 four times and not pressing any other number key.

13. *Twenty-eight.* Obtain 28 in the display by pressing 2 five times and not pressing any other number key.

14. *Thirty.* Obtain 30 in the display by pressing 3 three times and not pressing any other number key.

15. *Another thirty.* Obtain 30 in the display by pressing 3 four times and not pressing any other number key.

16. *And another thirty.* Obtain 30 in the display by pressing 6 three times and not pressing any other number key.

17. *Thirty-seven.* Obtain 37 in the display by pressing 3 five times and not pressing any other number key.

18. *One hundred.* Obtain 100 in the display by pressing 1 five times and not pressing any other number key.

19. *Another one hundred.* Obtain 100 in the display by pressing 5 five times and not pressing any other number key.

20. *And another one hundred.* Obtain 100 in the display by pressing six times the same number key and not pressing any other number key.

21. *Still another one hundred.* Obtain 100 in the display by pressing 9 six times and not pressing any other number key.

22. *And still another one hundred.* Obtain 100 in the display by pressing 5 six times and not pressing any other number key.

*FIGURE 3*

*An investment broker receives a telegram containing nothing but the number 57107735. What does the telegram say?*

23. *One hundred eleven.* Obtain 111 in the display by pressing no number keys other than 2.

24. *One thousand.* Obtain 1000 in the display by pressing no number keys other than 8.

25. *One to ten.* Obtain, in turn, the numbers 1 through 10 in the display by pressing 4 three or four times and not pressing any other number key.

26. *One to twenty.* Obtain, in turn, the numbers 1 through 20 in the display by pressing 2 five times (six times for 9 and 17) and not pressing any other number key.

27. *Building a number bridge.* Obtain 1234321 (a "number bridge") in the display by pressing ten times the same number key and not pressing any other number key.

28. *Cancelling multiplication by division in a strange way.* Obtain 3942 in the display by pressing once each of the number keys 739427, in that order, not pressing any other number key, and pressing no operation keys other than × and ÷ (multiplication by 7 is not allowed).

## 1-10. THE TALKING NUMBER PUZZLE

An investment broker received from one of his clients a telegram containing nothing but the number 57107735. He entered the number in the calculator, carefully examined the display, called his assistant, and gave him an order concerning the client's stocks. What was the order?

## 1-11. HOW TO MAKE YOUR OWN TRICKS AND PUZZLES

You can easily invent your own tricks and puzzles by using the collection of curious and little-known relations between numbers gathered together in the "Magician's Treasure Chest" chapter of this book. In fact, most of the tricks and puzzles just presented are based on this collection. And even if you do not wish to use this "Treasure Chest" for making new tricks and puzzles, just a mere verification of the numerical relations described therein will provide a pleasant and enlightening diversion for you and your friends.

## 1-12. ANSWERS

Representative solutions are given. No attempt has been made to compile a complete set of possible solutions.

1-4. The four pyramids puzzle

$$11 \times 11 = 121$$
$$111 \times 111 = 12321$$
$$1111 \times 1111 = 1234321$$
$$11111 \times 11111 = 123454321$$

1-7. The sailing fleet puzzle

$$3 \times 37 = 111$$
$$11 \times 101 = 1111$$
$$41 \times 271 = 11111$$
$$33 \times 3367 = 111111$$
$$239 \times 4649 = 1111111$$
$$1507 \times 7373 = 11111111$$
$$333 \times 333667 = 111111111$$
$$122221 \times 9091 = 1111111111$$

1-8. One, two, three ... one hundred

a. Simple direct sequence

$$1 + 2 + 34 - 5 + 67 - 8 + 9 = 100$$
$$1 + 23 - 4 + 56 + 7 + 8 + 9 = 100$$
$$12 - 3 - 4 + 5 - 6 + 7 + 89 = 100$$
$$12 + 3 + 4 + 5 - 6 - 7 + 89 = 100$$
$$123 + 4 - 5 + 67 - 89 = 100$$
$$123 - 45 - 67 + 89 = 100$$
$$123 + 45 - 67 + 8 - 9 = 100$$
$$1 \times 2 + 34 + 56 + 7 - 8 + 9 = 100$$

b. Simple reverse sequence

$$9 + 8 + 76 + 5 + 4 - 3 + 2 - 1 = 100$$
$$9 - 8 + 76 + 54 - 32 + 1 = 100$$
$$9 - 8 + 7 + 65 - 4 + 32 - 1 = 100$$
$$9 - 8 + 76 - 5 + 4 + 3 + 21 = 100$$
$$98 - 76 + 54 + 3 + 21 = 100$$
$$98 - 7 - 6 - 5 - 4 + 3 + 21 = 100$$
$$98 + 7 + 6 - 5 - 4 - 3 + 2 - 1 = 100$$
$$98 + 7 - 6 + 5 - 4 + 3 - 2 - 1 = 100$$

c. Simple mixed sequence

$$5823 \div 647 + 91 = 100$$
$$1578 \div 263 + 94 = 100$$
$$1428 \div 357 + 96 = 100$$

d. Algebraic sequence (for calculators with memory or with appropriate chain operation facility)

$$1 \div 2 + 38 \div 76 + 49 + 50 = 100$$
$$1 \times 2 \times 3 \times 4 + 5 + 6 + 7 \times 8 + 9 = 100$$
$$1 + 23 \times 4 - 5 + 6 + 7 + 8 - 9 = 100$$
$$1 \div 2 + 38 \div 76 + 5 + 94 = 100$$
$$1 \div 2 + 38 \div 76 + 4 + 95 = 100$$
$$12 \div 60 + 4 \div 5 + 3 + 9 + 87 = 100$$
$$3 \div 6 + 5 + 9 \div 18 + 24 + 70 = 100$$
$$3 \div 6 + 19 + 27 \div 54 + 80 = 100$$

1-9. Forbidden keys

1. $2 \div 2 = 1$, $22 \div 22 = 1$, etc.
2. $2 = (1 + 1) \div 1 = (3 + 3) \div 3$
   $= (4 + 4) \div 4$, etc.
3. (a) $3 = (1 + 1 + 1) \div 1 = (2 + 2 + 2) \div 2$
   $= (3 + 3 + 3) \div 3$, etc.
   (b) $3 = (4 \times 4 - 4) \div 4$
4. $(3 \times 3 + 3) \div 3 = 4$
5. $10 = (11 - 1) \div 1 = (22 - 2) \div 2$
   $= (33 - 3) \div 3$, etc.
6. $11 - 1 = 10$
7. $(3 \times 3 \times 3 + 3) \div 3 = 10$
8. $9 \div 9 + 9 = 10$

9. $22 \div 2 = 11$
10. $55 \div 5 + 5 = 16$
11. $22 + 2 = 24$
12. $(3 \times 3 \times 3) - 3 = 24$
13. $22 + 2 + 2 + 2 = 28$
14. $33 - 3 = 30$
15. $3 \times 3 \times 3 + 3 = 30$
16. $6 \times 6 - 6 = 30$
17. $333 \div 3 \div 3 = 37$
18. $111 - 11 = 100$
19. $(5 + 5 + 5 + 5) \times 5 = 100$
20. $100 = (111 - 11) \div 1 = (222 - 22) \div 2 = (333 - 33) \div 3$, etc.
21. $(99 \div 99) + 99 = 100$
22. $55 + 55 - 5 - 5 = 100$
23. $222 \div 2 = 111$
24. $1000 = 888 + 88 + 8 + 8 + 8 = (8888 - 888) \div 8$
25. $1 = 44 \div 44$;
    $2 = (4 + 4) \div 4$;
    $3 = (4 + 4 + 4) \div 4$ or $(4 \times 4 - 4) \div 4$;
    $4 = (4 - 4) \times 4 + 4$ or $4 + 4 - 4$;
    $5 = (4 \times 4 + 4) \div 4$;
    $6 = (4 + 4) \div 4 + 4$;
    $7 = (44 \div 4) - 4$;
    $8 = 4 + 4 + 4 - 4$ or $4 \times 4 - 4 - 4$;
    $9 = 4 \div 4 + 4 + 4$;
    $10 = (44 - 4) \div 4$.
26.— $2 \div 2 - 2 + 2 + 2 = 1$
    $2 + 2 + 2 - 2 - 2 = 2$

$$2 \div 2 + 2 + 2 - 2 = 3$$
$$2 \times 2 \times 2 - 2 - 2 = 4$$
$$-2 \div 2 + 2 + 2 + 2 = 5$$
$$2 + 2 + 2 + 2 - 2 = 6$$
$$22 \div 2 - 2 - 2 = 7$$
$$2 \times 2 \times 2 + 2 - 2 = 8$$
$$(2 \times 2 \times 2 \times 2 + 2) \div 2 = 9$$
$$2 + 2 + 2 + 2 + 2 = 10$$
$$22 \div 2 + 2 - 2 = 11$$
$$2 \times 2 \times 2 + 2 + 2 = 12$$
$$(22 + 2 + 2) \div 2 = 13$$
$$2 \times 2 \times 2 \times 2 - 2 = 14$$
$$22 \div 2 + 2 + 2 = 15$$
$$(2 \times 2 + 2 + 2) \times 2 = 16$$
$$22 \div 2 + 2 + 2 + 2 = 17$$
$$2 \times 2 \times 2 \times 2 + 2 = 18$$
$$-2 \div 2 - 2 + 22 = 19$$
$$22 + 2 - 2 - 2 = 20$$

27. $$\begin{aligned} 1234321 &= 1111 \times 1111 \div 1 \div 1 \\ &= 2222 \times 2222 \div 2 \div 2 \\ &= 3333 \times 3333 \div 3 \div 3 = \ldots \\ &= 9999 \times 9999 \div 9 \div 9 \end{aligned}$$

28. $73 \times 9 \times 42 \div 7 = 3942$

1-10. The talking number puzzle

Turn the calculator upside down. The number 57107735 will become the words "SELL OILS." Naturally, the broker ordered the client's oil stocks to be sold.

# 2 FASTER THAN THE CALCULATOR

An ability to perform rapid and complicated mental calculations has always been admired by those who see it demonstrated to them. This is why magicians frequently use various numerical tricks that give illusions of such an ability. Several tricks of this kind are described below.

## 2-1. INSTANTANEOUS ADDITION

Ask your friend to write down any two numbers. Then write a third yourself and say: "Let us see who can add these three numbers faster, you with the calculator or I with pencil and paper." By the time your friend enters the first number into the calculator you will have already written down the answer.

The secret of this trick lies in the fact that the number that you write is not just any number, but a number each digit of which you make to be equal to 9 less the corresponding digit of your friend's second (or first) number. Since $9 = 10 - 1$, $99 = 100 - 1$, and, in general, $9..9 = 10..0 - 1$, the sum of the three numbers is simply the first (second) number, plus 10..0 with as many zeros as there are digits in the second (first) number, minus 1.

Let us suppose that your friend writes down two numbers of the form ABCD... and KLMN. You write a number of the form*

$$(9-K)(9-L)(9-M)(9-N).$$

The sum is then ABCD... + 10000 − 1.

*Example*

*a.* Your friend writes 175485 and 2346. You write 7653 and quickly compute the sum: $175485 + 10000 - 1 = 185484$.

*b.* Your friend writes 175485 and 2346. You write 824514 and quickly compute the sum: $1000000 + 2346 - 1 = 1002345$.

*Trick formula*

$$\text{ABCD...} + \text{KLMN} + (9-K)(9-L)(9-M)(9-N) = \text{ABCD...} + 10000 - 1.$$

*We use notations like ABCD, (9—K)(9—L)(9—M)(9—N), etc., to indicate numbers whose digits are A, B, C, and D or (9—K),(9—L),(9—M), and (9—N), etc. These notations should not be confused with products such as A x B x C x D; we always use the multiplication sign "x" to indicate a product.

*FIGURE 4*

*The number on this man's flag identifies an item of his clothing. What item is it?*

## 2-2. ANOTHER INSTANTANEOUS ADDITION

Ask your friend to write down several three- or four-digit numbers and to pass them to you. Then write yourself as many three- or four-digit numbers and say: "Let us see who can add all these numbers faster, you with the calculator or I with pencil and paper." In a second or two write down the answer and then wait "impatiently" until your friend obtains it with the calculator.

The secret of this trick lies in the fact that also here you make each digit of the numbers that you write equal to 9 less the corresponding digit of one of his numbers. The sum is therefore 1000 (or 10000) minus 1, multiplied by the number of the numbers written by your friend.

Let us suppose that your friend writes down two three-digit numbers, each of the form ABC. You write likewise two numbers, each of which has the form

$$(9 - A)(9 - B)(9 - C).$$

The sum is then $(1000 - 1) \times 2 = 2000 - 2 = 1998$. The trick will obviously work with numbers other than three- or four-digit ones. However, it is less effective if fewer than three digits are used, and the many 9's which appear in the answer when very large numbers are employed will make your friend suspect that your numbers are very special numbers.

Observe that there is no need to match your friend's numbers one by one. That is, each digit that you use in any one of your numbers may be computed from a similarly positioned digit in any of your friend's numbers, care being taken that none of your friend's digits is used more than once, and that each of his digits is represented by one of yours.

*Example*

*a.* Your friend writes 453 and 236. You write (matching each number with one of yours) 546 and 763 and quickly compute the sum: $(1000 - 1) \times 2 = 2000 - 2 = 1998$.

*b.* Your friend writes 453 and 236. You write (using the digits from the two numbers in alternation) 566 and 743 and quickly compute the sum: $(1000 - 1) \times 2 = 2000 - 2 = 1998$.

*Trick formula*

$$ABC + (9-A)(9-B)(9-C) = 1000 - 1$$

## 2-3. AND ANOTHER FAST ADDITION

Ask your friend to enter in the calculator a number of his choice having up to six digits and to multiply this number by one or more numbers of your choice so that a seven- or eight-digit number is produced. Ask him to write down the result. Now ask him to enter in the calculator a number of your choice and to multiply it by one or more numbers of his choice so that another seven- or eight-digit number is produced. Ask him to attach this number to the previously obtained number so as to form a "joint" number having fourteen to sixteen digits. Next (this step is optional) ask him to attach one or two digits of his choice to the final number on either or both sides of it, and attach one or two digits to the number yourself. Now say: "Without using the calculator I shall add all the digits of this number, then I shall add the digits of the digit sum, and so on, until I obtain a single digit. Let us see if you can determine the final digit with the calculator faster than I can by a mental calculation." After your friend presses several keys of the calculator you can declare that you already have the answer.

The secret of this trick lies in the fact that the final digit sum of any number which is a multiple of 9 is 9 and that, if several new digits are attached to such a number, then the final digit sum of the resulting number is the same as the final digit sum of the attached digits.

The true purpose of the operations which your friend performs under your "direction" is to produce a "joint" number which is a multiple of 9. Such a number will always be produced provided that: (a) the product of the numbers by which you request your friend to multiply the number of his choice is a multiple of 9, and (b) the number of your choice which you give to your friend is a multiple of 9. The final digit sum of the "joint" number obtained under these conditions is therefore either 9 (if no digits are attached to the number) or is equal to the final digit sum of the attached digits.

*Example*

*a.* Your friend enters 357 as the number of his choice. You ask him to multiply it by 27 and 201 (27 is a multiple of 9). The result is 1937439. Next, you give to him as the number of your choice the number 3546, for example, (which is a multiple of 9, since its digit sum $3 + 5 + 4 + 6 = 18$ is a multiple of 9). Your friend decides to multiply your number by 61 and 5. The result is 1081530. Then he puts the two numbers together, producing the "joint" number 10815301937439, and attaches 49 to it. You attach 8 to the other side. The final number is

$$4910815301937439 8.$$

Since the final digit sum of the attached digits is 3 (because $4 + 9 + 8 = 21$, and $2 + 1 = 3$), you will declare that the final digit sum of the entire number is 3.

*b.* You choose to leave the "joint" number 10815301937439 as it is. Without performing any calculation, you will declare that the final digit sum of this number is 9.

*Trick formula*

Final digit sum of AB..(M × 9)(N × 9)..CD is the same as that of AB....CD. Final digit sum of $(M \times 9)(N \times 9)$ is 9.

## 2-4. FAST MULTIPLICATION

Ask your friend to write down any three- or four-digit number and to give it to you. Pass to him your calculator and ask him to multiply his number by 999 (9999 for a four-digit number). When he is finished say: "Why did it take you so long? I had the answer a long time ago without any calculator. The answer is ...."

This trick is based on a special property of the numbers 9, 99, 999, 9999, etc. Let ABCD be a four-digit number. The product of ABCD and 9999 is an eight-digit number of the form

$$ABC(D-1)(9-A)(9-B)(9-C)(10-D),$$

where the last four digits are obtained from the first four by subtracting them from 9. Analogous expressions hold for three-digit numbers and for other numbers.

*Example*

Your friend writes 3654. Using the above formula, you compute either mentally or on paper the number 36536346 as the product of 3654 and 9999.

*Trick formula*

$$ABCD \times 9999$$
$$=ABC(D-1)(9-A)(9-B)(9-C)(10-D)$$

*FIGURE 5*

*The numbers 3869 and 6205 may be called an "amicable pair" because* $38 \times 38 + 69 \times 69 = 6205$ *and* $62 \times 62 + 05 \times 05 = 3869$. *Can you find other amicable pairs of numbers?*

*Exceptions*

If the number ends with a zero, the result is

$$\text{ABC0} \times 9999$$
$$= \text{AB}(\text{C}-1)9(9-\text{A})(9-\text{B})(10-\text{C})0.$$

If the number ends with two zeros, the result is

$$\text{AB00} \times 9999$$
$$= \text{A}(\text{B}-1)99(9-\text{A})(10-\text{B})00.$$

Analogous relations hold for numbers with other numbers of digits and other numbers of zeros.

## 2-5. ANOTHER FAST MULTIPLICATION

The preceding trick can be made even more spectacular by performing the multiplication by 9..9 in several steps. This will also give you more time for completing your calculations. For example, in the case of a four-digit number you can ask your friend to multiply the number, in a chain operation, by 99 and 101, or by 3, 33, and 101, or by 9, 11, and 101, etc. In the case of a three-digit number you can ask him to multiply it by 27 and 37, by 3 and 333, or by 3, 9, and 37, etc.

*Example*

Your friend writes 295. You ask him to

multiply it by 3, 9, and 37. Since $3 \times 9 \times 37 = 999$, the answer is 294705, which you can compute either mentally or on paper.

*Trick formula*

$$ABC \times (999 \text{ as product})$$
$$= AB(C-1)(9-A)(9-B)(10-C)$$

## 2-6. FAST DIVISION

The preceding trick can be reversed. Ask your friend to write a two-, three-, or four-digit number. Attach an equal number of digits to his number and ask him to divide the resulting number by 9..9 with as many 9's as was the number of digits in the original number. As soon as he presses several keys of the calculator you can say: "I wish they would build faster calculators. I computed the answer mentally a long time ago. The answer is ....."

This trick is based on the fact that the digits attached by you to your friend's number are such that the new number is of the form

$$AB(9-A)(9-B),$$
$$ABC(9-A)(9-B)(9-C),$$

or

$$ABCD(9-A)(9-B)(9-C)(9-D),$$

depending on whether your friend wrote a two-,

three-, or four-digit number. As it is clear from the preceding examples, a division of these numbers by 99, 999, or 9999 yields A(B + 1), AB(C + 1), and ABC(D + 1), respectively. Note that you can attach your digits in front as well as behind your friend's number. As before, you can ask him to divide the final number in succession by several numbers whose product is the 9..9 number. Or, instead, you can ask him to divide the final number by 3..3 or by several numbers whose product is the 3..3 number. In this case the answer will be three times as large as when the division by 9..9 is used. Moreover, if you see that the answer will be an even number, you can ask your friend to perform an additional division by 2. The final answer will then be one half that number.

*Example*

*a.* Your friend writes 754. You modify this number to 245754. Division by 999 yields 246. Additional division by 2 yields 123.

*b.* Your friend writes 874. You modify this number to 258741 and ask your friend to divide it, in a chain operation, by 37 and then by 9 (whose product is 333). While your friend enters the numbers into the calculator, you compute the answer: $259 \times 3 = 777$.

*Trick formula*

$$ABC(9 - A)(9 - B)(9 - C) \div 999 = AB(C + 1)$$

## 2-7. ANOTHER FAST DIVISION

The preceding trick can be modified by asking your friend to display the number made up from his and your digits and to divide it by the number that you used for its construction plus 1. The result of the division will then be the number 9..9. Furthermore, if you ask your friend to perform an additional division by some of the numbers whose product is 9..9, the result will be the remaining part of the product.

*Example*

*a.* Your friend writes 739. You modify it to 260739 and ask him to divide this number by 261. The result will be 999.

*b.* Your friend writes 739. You modify it to 260739 and ask him to divide this number, in a chain operation, by 261 and 27. Since $999 = 27 \times 37$, the result will be 37.

*Trick formula*

$$ABC(9 - A)(9 - B)(9 - C) \div AB(C + 1) = 999$$

## 2-8. THE 109..989 MULTIPLICATION AND DIVISION

Ask your friend to enter in the calculator one of the "flip-flop" numbers discussed in Section 1-5 and ask him to tell you his "favorite" one-digit number. Now say: "Multiply (divide) the number in the calculator by your favorite number and divide (multiply) by ...., which is my favorite number. I shall tell you the answer just as soon as you obtain it with the calculator."

The secret of this trick lies in the special property of the numbers 109..989 as a result of which a multiplication of such a number by a one-digit number is equivalent to the addition of this one-digit number less 1 to the two first digits of the number 109..989 and subtraction of this one-digit number less 1 from the two last digits of it. The number which you present to your friend in this trick is a multiple of 109..989 that you construct in accordance with this property, and your "favorite" number that you communicate to your friend is the multiplier. Therefore, when your friend multiplies the number displayed in the calculator by his "favorite" number and divides it by your "favorite" number he, in effect, merely multiplies the number 109..989 by his "favorite" number. You can easily find the final product by using the equivalent addition and subtraction or by using the formula given below.

*Note:* If your friend's "favorite" number happens to be the multiplier that you used for constructing the number presented to him, you will have to ask him to divide the number in the calculator by his "favorite" number and to multiply it by your "favorite" number, which can be any one-digit number. The final result will then be the number 109..989 multiplied by the latter number.

*Example*

*a.* You ask your friend to enter in the calculator the number 4356, which is 1089 × 4. He tells you that his favorite number is 7. You tell him that your favorite number is 4 and ask him to multiply 4356 by 7 and to divide by 4, which is the same as multiplying 1089 by 7. Adding 6 (that is, 7 — 1) to the digits 1 and 0 and subtracting 6 from the digits 8 and 9, you quickly find the answer: 7623.

*b.* You ask your friend to enter in the calculator the number 219978, which is 109989 × 2. Your friend tells you that his favorite number is 2. Since this happens to be the multiplier used by you for constructing 219978, you ask your friend to *divide* 219978 by his favorite number and to *multiply* it by yours, 9, for example. The result will be 109989 × 9, which you quickly compute by using the above rule (or by means of the formula given below) to be 989901.

*Trick formula*

(1) $109..989 \times A = A(A-1)9..9(9-A)(10-A)$
(2) $A(A-1)9..9(9-A)(10-A) \times B \div A$
$= B(B-1)\,9..9\,(9-B)(10-B)$

## 2-9. THE MARTIAN MONEY PUZZLE

Three astronauts who just arrived on Mars found a strange sheet of paper with various

*FIGURE 6*

*Three astronauts who just arrived on Mars found the Martian money bill shown here. They tore it into three pieces. Can you tell which piece represents the smallest amount of Martian money? Which represents the largest amount? What can the astronauts do with the three pieces to divide the money evenly among themselves?* [*See story in Section 2-9*].

numbers printed on it. Not knowing what the sheet meant, they tore it into three pieces, as shown in Fig. 6, so that each astronaut would have part of it as a souvenir. The next morning a local boy told them that what they had found was a Martian money bill, and that this type of bill was used by cutting out a desired number (desired amount of Martian dollars) from any horizontal row of numbers. For example, if one were to cut out the numbers 4, 3, 2, and 1, the four pieces would constitute a total of $4 + 3 + 2 + 1 = 10$ Martian dollars; on the other hand, if one were to cut out the number 4321 in one piece, the piece would constitute 4,321 Martian dollars. The three astronauts immediately proceeded to calculate how much Martian money each of them ended up with, and soon discovered that each had a different amount. They decided then to divide the money evenly among themselves, but so that each would have as much money as possible, and that their three pieces of the original bill would be cut in as few pieces as possible. Such is the story.

Now the puzzle. (1) Without using the calculator, tell which of the three parts of the torn bill represented the smallest amount (you can answer this question "faster than the calculator"). (2) Use your calculator to find the actual amount that each part represented. (3) Figure out how the astronauts finally divided the Martian money bill among themselves.

# 3

# MYSTIC NUMBER 142857

The number 142857 has many remarkable properties which can be utilized for performing a variety of exceptionally beautiful and spectacular numerical tricks. Several examples of such tricks are presented in this chapter. The following relations may help you to memorize this amazing number, which is intimately related to the number 7:

(a) Obtaining the number from the number 7 through multiplication and addition

$$2 \times 7 \times 10000 + 2 \times 2 \times 7 \times 100 + 2 \times 2 \times 2 \times 7 + 1 = 142857$$

(b) Obtaining the number from the number 7 through division

$$999999 \div 7 = 142857$$

(c) The number can be easily constructed by noticing that its first two digits, 14, are twice the number 7; its second two digits, 28, are twice the first two; its last two digits, 57, are twice the second two plus 1.

## 3-1. THE STUBBORN DIGITS

Ask your friend what kind of numbers, such as odd, even, prime, whole, rational, etc., he knows. Then tell him that he has left out the "stubborn digits" numbers. Since no such numbers really exist (we invented the name for the purpose of this trick), he will probably argue that there is no such thing. Pass your calculator to him and tell him that 142857 is an example of a stubborn digits number because it "does not like to give up any of its digits." To prove your statement, ask him to multiply this number by 3. The result will be 428571, which is the original number with the digit 1 moved over to the right. Then ask him to multiply the number 142857 by 2. The result will be 285714, which, again, is the original number with the digits 1 and 4 moved over to the right. Next ask him to multiply it by 6, 4, and 5. Each time one digit will move to the right, but no original digits will disappear and none will be added. This should prove your point. Now, having convinced your friend that 142857 is a stubborn digits number indeed, ask him what will happen if he multiplies it by 7. Let him do the multiplication. He is in for a surprise.

*Example*

| | |
|---|---|
| 142857 × 3 = 428571 | 142857 × 4 = 571428 |
| 142857 × 2 = 285714 | 142857 × 5 = 714285 |
| 142857 × 6 = 857142 | 142857 × 7 = 999999 |

## 3-2. THE STUCK CALCULATOR

If you think that your friend will not mind a little mischief on your part, you can do the following trick. Tell your friend that you are afraid that your calculator is "stuck" and ask him, in order to "check" the calculator, to enter in it the number 142857 and to perform the first operation shown below. The result will be the same number 142857. Then say: "I was afraid so. It seems that the calculator is stuck." Then, to "double-check" the calculator, tell him to perform the second operation shown below. The result will be again the same. Now say: "Too bad. It seems to be stuck completely." Then, "just in case," ask him to perform the third operation, and so on, until all five operations are completed. Then ask him to multiply the number 142857 (which is still in the calculator display) by 7. The result will be 999999. Now say: "It seems to be getting unstuck," and ask your friend to add 0.99 and then to divide the result by 8.1. The number 123456.78 will appear in the display.

You can now declare that the calculator is "unstuck" and is ready for further calculations.

*Example*

$$[(142857 \times 3) - 1] \div 10 + 100000 = 142857$$
$$[(142857 \times 2) - 14] \div 100 + 30000 + 110000 = 142857$$
$$[(142857 \times 6) - 142] \div 1000 + 30000 + 112000 = 142857$$
$$[(142857 \times 4) - 1428] \div 10000 + 30600 + 112200 = 142857$$
$$[(142857 \times 5) - 14285] \div 100000 + 31620 + 111230 = 142857$$
$$142857 \times 7 = 999999$$

## 3-3. THE 142857 ADDITION

Ask your friend to display in the calculator the number 142857 (or any of its transpositions obtained by moving one or more of its first digits all the way to the right). Then ask him to add to this number the number 428571 (or another suitable transposition of the original number). Now say: "Why are you so slow? I can do this simple addition without the calculator a lot faster than you do it with the calculator. The answer is ....."

The secret of this trick lies in the fact that the sum of two transpositions of the number

142857 is also a transposition of this number, except when the sum of the last digits of the two transpositions does not yield one of the digits contained in 142857, or when the sum of the first digits exceeds 9 (be sure not to use transpositions of the latter type except when the sum is 999999; see the note below). Therefore, to find the sum of the two transpositions, you need merely to identify the transposition that ends on the digit representing the sum of the last digits of the two transpositions.

To do this trick as smoothly as possible, you should write the number 142857 and keep it in front of you so as to be able to write any of its transpositions without any hesitation.

*Note:* If the sum of the last digits is 9, the sum of the two transpositions is 999999.

*Example*

*a.* You ask your friend to add 142857 and 285714. Since $7 + 4 = 11$, the last digit of the sum is 1, and therefore the transposition constituting this sum is 428571.

*b.* You ask your friend to add 142857 and 857142. Since $2 + 7 = 9$, the sum is 999999.

*Trick formula*

The sum of two transpositions of 142857 is also a transposition of 142857 except as explained above.

## 3-4. THE 142857 SUBTRACTION

A trick similar to the one just described can be performed by subtracting two transpositions of the number 142857. As before, the difference is another transposition of the same number.

*Example*

You ask your friend to enter 571428 and to subtract 285714. Since 8 — 4 = 4, the answer is 285714.

*Trick formula*

The difference of two transpositions of 142857 is also a transposition of 142857 except as explained above.

## 3-5. THE HIDDEN 142857 ADDITION AND SUBTRACTION

Since the number 142857 can be obtained by division (999999 ÷ 7, etc.) or by multiplication (11 × 13 × 27 × 37, etc.), you can make the last two tricks even more spectacular if you ask your friend first to perform the above division or multiplication and then to add or subtract a transposition of 142857 of your choice.

*Example*

*a.* You ask your friend to divide 999999 by 7 and to add 428571. To find the answer, add 7 (the last digit in 142857) and 1 (the last digit in the number to be added). Since $7 + 1 = 8$, the answer, being a transposition of 142857 ending with 8, is 571428.

*b.* You ask your friend to multiply $2 \times 11 \times 13 \times 27 \times 37$ (the product is $2 \times 142857$, which is 285714) and to subtract 142857. Since $14 - 7 = 7$, the answer is 142857.

*Trick formula*

A transposition of 142857 added (subtracted) to (from) a transposition of 142857 obtained as a product of several numbers is another transposition of 142857 except as explained above.

## 3-6. THE 142857 MULTIPLICATION

Even more impressive tricks can be performed by using the number 142857. Ask your friend to enter any one- or two-digit number into the calculator and to tell you what this number is (the trick will work with numbers having more digits, but larger numbers will probably overload your calculator). Then ask your friend to multiply it by $11 \times 13 \times 27 \times 37$ (the product is 142857). Now say: "I wish they would build faster calculators. I computed the answer in my head a long time ago. Let's see if you will get the right answer; it should be ....."

Here is the explanation of this trick. The product of 142857 and any other number can be easily found by using the following rules:

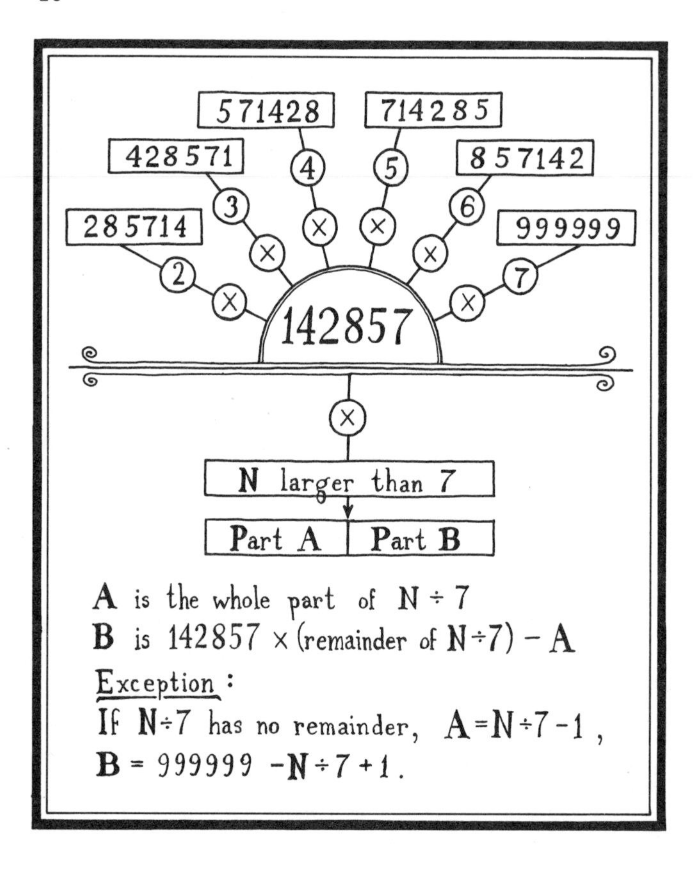


*FIGURE 7*

*Multiplication of 142857 by any number can be easily accomplished with the aid of this diagram.*

1. Multiplication of 142857 by 2, 3, 4, 5, or 6 yields a transposition of 142857 ending with the digit 4, 1, 8, 5, or 2, respectively.

2. Multiplication by 7 yields 999999.

3. Multiplication by any other number, N, yields a number the first digits of which represent the whole part of N ÷ 7. The remaining digits represent the number 142857 multiplied by the remainder of N ÷ 7, less the whole part of N ÷ 7. However:

4. If N ÷ 7 has no remainder, the first digits are N ÷ 7 — 1, the remaining digits are 999999 — N ÷ 7 + 1.

*Example*

*a.* Your friend enters 3 in the calculator. By Rule 1, the answer is 428571.

*b.* Your friend enters 31. Apply Rule 3. Since 31 ÷ 7 = 4 + 3/7, and since 142857 × 3 — 4 = 428567, the answer is 4428567.

*c.* Your friend enters 35. Apply Rule 4. Since 35 ÷ 7 = 5, the first digit of the answer is 4. Since 999999 — 5 + 1 = 999995, the answer is 4999995.

*Trick formula*

The formula is contained in Fig. 7.

In order to perform this trick as smoothly as possible, make a pause after your friend tells you what number he has entered into the calculator. During this pause you can work out part of your calculations (for example, find the whole part and the remainder of N ÷ 7). Then you can complete the calculations while your friend does the remaining operations. Naturally, you can modify the trick by using another technique for introducing the number 142857. For example, you can ask your friend to multiply his number by 999999 and to divide by 7, to multiply and divide by any series of numbers producing 142857 in the final result, etc.

## 3-7. THE MAGIC-DIGITS MULTIPLICATION

In this spectacular trick instantaneous calculations are performed with a touch of magic. The trick is both beautiful and mystifying.

Ask your friend to tell you his two "favorite" one-digit numbers and how many times he wishes them to appear in the calculator (for a calculator with an eight-digit display the two numbers can appear a maximum of four times); let this number be N. Next ask him to enter 1 in the calculator and to add to this 1 any part of the number 14285714285 comprising at least N digits. Now say: "I shall mentally work out a program involving not more than three operations — one multiplication, one possible addition, and one possible subtraction — that will convert the number now displayed in the calculator into your favorite numbers and will make them appear in the display exactly as many times as you said you wanted them to appear." In a few moments you can tell your friend the program, and upon completing this program he will see his numbers in the display just as you said he would.

The secret of this trick lies in the fact that when a number equal to 1 plus a part of the number 14285714285 is multiplied by a number of the form 7..7, whose number of digits is the same or smaller than that in the number to be multiplied, the result is always a number of the form A..A0..0B..B having the following properties:

1. The number of digits in it is equal to the total number of digits in the two numbers that are multiplied.
2. The number of zeros in it is equal to the number of digits in the multiplicand less the number of digits in the multiplier.
3. The digits A and B appear as many times as there are digits in the multiplier.
4. The digit A is equal to the first digit of the product 7 × (1 plus the first digit of the multiplicand).
5. The digit B is equal to the last digit of the product 7 × (the last digit of the multiplicand).

According to Property 3, you can generate a number of the form A..A0..0B..B with the required number of the digits A and B from the number displayed in the calculator by asking your friend to multiply it by a number 7..7

having the same number of digits as is required for A or B. Furthermore, since you can easily determine the digits A and B by using Properties 4 and 5, you can accomplish a conversion of the number A..A0..0B..B into a number whose digits are those specified by your friend by asking him to perform a simple addition, subtraction, or both.

*Note:* If one of your friend's "favorite" numbers is 9, you can modify the trick as follows. Instead of asking your friend to enter 1 and to add any part of the number 14285714285, ask him to enter a part of this number ending with the digit 8 and to attach to it the digit 7. Then proceed as before. A multiplication by 7..7 will now yield a number of the form A..A0..09..9 whose properties are the same as those enumerated above except that its last digits are 9's.

*Example*

*a.* Your friend's favorite numbers are 5 and 9, and he wishes each of them to appear three times. You ask him to enter 1 in the calculator and to add to this 1 a part of the number 14285714285 containing three digits or more. Let us suppose that he selects 2857. Added to 1, it produces 2858 in the display. Since his numbers must appear three times, you ask him to multiply the number in the calculator by 777, while you quickly calculate the product by using Properties 4 and 5. The calculation is as follows: adding 1 to the first digit of 2858 and multiplying by 7, you obtain $(2+1) \times 7 = 21$, which means that the first digit of the product is 2; multiplying the last digit of 2858 by 7, you obtain 56, so that the last digit of the product is 6; the number of digits in the product, by Property 1, is 7; hence the product is 2220666. You recognize that this number can be converted into the number containing your friend's favorite digits, 5 and 9, simply by adding to it the number 3330333 and tell your friend to do so.

*b.* Your friend declares that his favorite numbers are 5 and 9 and that he wishes them to appear four times in the calculator. You ask him to select from the number 14285714285 three or more consecutive digits ending with 8. He selects 428. You ask him to enter 428 in the calculator and to attach 7. The result is 4287. You ask him to multiply this number by 7777 and to add 22220000. The result is 55559999.

*Trick formula*

$$[1 + (\text{any part of } 14285714285)] \times 7..7 = \text{A..A0..0B..B};$$
$$(\text{last part of } 14285714287) \times 7..7 = \text{A..A0..09..9}.$$

The number of digits in the multiplier may not be larger than that in the multiplicand. The digits A and B are found as explained above.

# 4

# PLAYING GAMES

Mathematical games are among the oldest and the most interesting "intellectual" games ever invented. Four thousand years ago they were played by the ancient Egyptians, and as long as six thousand years ago they were played by the ancient Chinese. In the middle ages they were played at public tournaments. Until now, mathematical games frequently required rather lengthy calculations, which usually had little to do with the substance of the games and merely impeded their natural progress. The pocket calculator, with its ability to produce instantaneous answers to various numerical problems, now for the first time makes it possible to play these games with unprecedented speed and unabiding interest. The number of the various presently known mathematical games is quite large, and many of them can be played with the calculator. Descriptions of such games can be found in most books on mathematical pastimes and entertainments. Here we shall not attempt to describe them to any degree of completeness. Instead, we shall merely give two representative examples of such games. One of them, the "Martian Money" game, is a new game, designed by the author specifically for playing with the aid of a pocket calculator. The other, the "One Hundred" game, is an old one, but is also admirably suited for playing with the pocket calculator.

## 4-1. THE ONE HUNDRED GAME

This game is more than three hundred years old. A French mathematician discussed its strategy in a book published in 1613. Another French author, in a book published in 1786, attributed its invention to two travelers, who invented and played it to lessen the tedium of a long journey. The game is usually for two players and, when played by using a calculator, is as follows.

One player "deposits" (enters) in the calculator any number smaller than a certain previously agreed upon number called the "ceiling." The second player adds to the deposited number his own deposit, likewise smaller than the ceiling. Then the first player adds another deposit (again smaller than the ceiling) to the sum, and so on, until the total deposit becomes 100. The player who makes the final deposit, producing 100 in the calculator display, wins the game.

*Example*

Let the ceiling (as agreed upon by the players) be 11. Player A deposits 7, say. B deposits 10. Then A makes a deposit, and so on until, for example, the accumulated deposit is 75 and it is B's turn to make the next deposit. B now deposits 3, A deposits 5, B deposits 6, A deposits 1, B deposits 10 and wins.

The "One Hundred" game as just described can always be won by the player who makes the first deposit if the ceiling is to his advantage and if he uses a proper strategy. On the other hand, it can always be won by the player who makes the second deposit if the ceiling is to his advantage and if he uses a correct strategy. The winning strategy is based on the three elements: the winning first deposit, the winning subsequent deposits, and the winning positions (accumulated deposits).

The winning first deposit is equal to the remainder obtained when 100 is divided by the ceiling. A winning position is any multiple of the ceiling plus the winning first deposit. A winning deposit is that which puts a player into a winning position. For example, if the ceiling is 11, the winning first deposit is the remainder of $100 \div 11$, or 1. The winning positions are 12,

23, 34, 45, 56, 67, 78, and 89. The winning deposits are those which bring the accumulated deposits to 12, 23, etc. In this example nothing can prevent the first player from winning if he deposits 1 on his first move and maintains the winning positions thereafter. On the other hand, if the ceiling is 10, for example, the winning first deposit is 0, but since the first player must deposit at least 1, he cannot prevent the second player from occupying the winning positions (which in this case are 10, 20, 30, 40, 50, 60, 70, 80, and 90) throughout the game and finally winning the game.

Naturally, if you are playing this game with someone to whom you do not want to disclose the winning strategy right away, you should not take a winning position early in the game because your opponent will then easily learn the strategy himself.

Since there is no way of preventing one of the players from occupying a winning position on his first move (assuming that he knows the proper strategy), the "One Hundred" game is not a fair contest. Therefore certain modifications must be introduced to make the game honest.

First of all, one can use a number larger than 100 as the goal, and one can use a correspondingly larger number as the ceiling. The winning first deposit and the winning positions are then found in the same way as for the regular "One Hundred" game. For example, if the goal is 978, and the ceiling is 150, the winning initial deposit is 78, and the winning positions are 228, 378, 528, 678, and 828. However, since larger numbers must now be used for deposits, and since the winning numbers are now more difficult to memorize and to compute, there is a good chance that one of the players will make a mistake which can be used by the second player to his advantage.

Secondly, one can play the game with "obstacles." In this case the deposits are limited to some specified numbers, such as 1, 3, 5, and 7, for example, or, at the time of a deposit, are limited to numbers that do not place a player in a winning position, or may not be the same number two times in a row, or are limited to numbers larger than a certain smallest number, etc.

Thirdly, the game can be played by more than two persons, in which case the outcome of the game cannot be predicted.

## 4-2. THE MARTIAN MONEY GAME

The game may be explained with the help of the following story (also see the "Martian Money Puzzle" in Chapter 2).

Two astronauts, while vacationing on the planet Mars, were each given one Martian money bill by their friendly Martian host. Each bill consisted of a strip of paper with a series of numbers printed on it, as shown in Fig. 8. According to Martian rules, this type of bill was used by cutting out numbers from it to produce the needed sum of Martian dollars. During their stay on Mars each astronaut spent the same amount of his Martian money for buying souvenirs, and each kept part of the money for taking it back to Earth to show to his family. However, just when they were about to board their space ship for the trip home, they were told by Martian customs officials that they must pay an export tax on the Martian money which they were taking with them. The tax, according to Martian laws, equaled the sum of the digits in the number representing the sum of the Martian dollars to be exported. Having paid the tax, the astronauts departed from Mars and soon arrived at their base on Earth. Just when they were about to leave the base, they were told by a local customs official that an import tax was due on the Martian money in their possession. The tax had to be paid in Martian dollars, and as before, in the amount equal to the sum of the digits in the number representing the sum of the Martian dollars in their possession. The astronauts paid the import tax and soon arrived at the airport for a flight to their hometown. However, just as they were about to board their airplane, they were approached by an official of the Department of Internal Revenue, who informed them that an income tax was due on the Martian money which they had in their

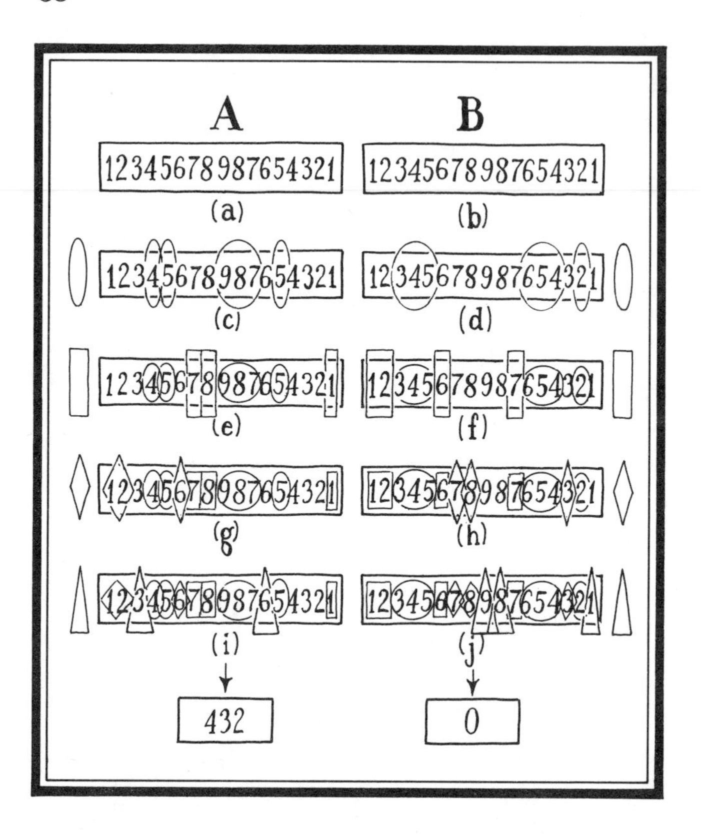


*FIGURE 8*

*The Martian money game is an exciting new game that can be played by several people.*

possession. The tax was to be paid in Martian dollars in the amount determined by the same rule as before. The astronauts cheerfully paid the income tax and then counted their money to see how much was left. A strange thing happened. Although they started with identical Martian money bills, although they spent an equal amount of Martian dollars on the souvenirs, and although each paid taxes in accordance with exactly the same rules, one of them ended up with more Martian money than the other, thus being the winner in the "Martian Money" game.

*Example*

Each astronaut started with identical Martian money bills, Fig. 8a,b. Let us assume that each spent 1001 Martian dollars (m.d.) on the souvenirs. Their payments are tabulated below.

| Astronaut A paid (Fig. 8c) | Astronaut B paid (Fig. 8d) |
|---|---|
| 4+5+987+5=1001 m.d. | 345+654+2=1001 m.d. |
| A has now left | B has now left |
| 123+678+6+4321= | 12+678987+3+1= |
| 5128 m.d. | 679003 m.d. |
| A's export tax is | B's export tax is |
| 5+1+2+8=16 m.d. | 6+7+9+3=25 m.d. |
| A pays (Fig. 8e) | B pays (Fig. 8f) |
| 7+8+1=16 m.d. | 12+6+7=25 m.d. |
| A has now left | B has now left |
| 123+6+6+432=567 m.d. | 7898+3+1=7902 m.d. |
| A's import tax is | B's import tax is |
| 5+6+7=18 m.d. | 7+9+2=18 m.d. |
| A pays (Fig. 8g) | B pays (Fig. 8h) |

12+6=18 m.d.
A has now left
3+6+432=441 m.d.
A's income tax is
4+4+1=9 m.d.
A pays (Fig. 8i)
3+6=9 m.d.
and takes home 432 m.d.

7+8+3=18 m.d.
B has now left
98+1=99 m.d.
B's income tax is
9+9=18 m.d.
B pays (Fig. 8j)
9+8+1=18 m.d.
and has nothing left to take home.

## 4-3. HOW TO PLAY THE MARTIAN MONEY GAME

1. The game can be played by any number of players. Each starts with the same "bill" (Fig. 8 a,b) that he draws on a sheet of paper.

2. The players agree on a method to determine the price of the souvenir. For instance, they may want to limit the price to one-, two-, three-, or four-digit numbers. In this case they prepare ten slips of paper with the numbers 0, 1, 2, 3, 4, 5, 6, 7, 8, and 9. The numbers are mixed, and one of them is drawn to determine the first digit of the purchase price number. The numbers are then mixed again, and one of them is drawn to determine the second digit of the purchase price number, and so on until the purchase price is found. For example, if they agreed that the purchase price was to have four digits, and the numbers drawn were 3, 0, 4, and 9, the price is 3049 m.d.

3. Each player pays for the souvenir and then pays the three taxes, as explained in the

above example, by crossing out certain digits from the original bill. For clarity, the digits used for paying the purchase price and the three taxes are marked with circles, squares, diamonds, and triangles, respectively, as shown in Fig. 8.

4. After each round of the game, the player who has the largest sum of m.d. left in his possession adds the excess of it over the corresponding sums left in the possession of all other players. For example, if player A is left with a total of 500 m.d., player B with 300 m.d., and player C with 75 m.d., A writes down 200 + 425 = 625 m.d. as his score for the round.

5. To give each player an even chance of accumulating equivalent scores, the same purchase price is repeated for as many rounds of the game as there are players.

6. The winner of the game is the player with the largest total score after the last round of the game.

7. If so agreed, the game can be played with each player starting with two Martian money bills, rather than with one. Larger purchase prices can then be used, and the game becomes even more interesting.

8. If so agreed, the players may play the game with a "standard exemption" applied to the import or income tax or to both these taxes. For a one-digit tax, the standard exemption is always equal to the second largest figure (8, 7, etc.) appearing on the Martian

money still in possession of the player claiming the exemption. For a two-digit tax, the standard exemption is the sum of the two largest figures on the Martian money still in his possession. Depending on initial agreement, the claiming of exemption may be optional or mandatory.

9. If a player has no money left after the payment of the first (export) tax, the winner triples his score against this player. The winner doubles his score against a player who has no money left after the payment of the second (import) tax.

# 5

# PYRAMID DIVERSIONS

The diversions described in this chapter can be used in two ways. First, they can be used as games or entertainments. Second, they can be used for building up one's skills in achieving unusual and surprising numerical effects, that constitute an essential part of various numerical tricks and recreations.

## 5-1. CLIMBING THE FIRST NUMBER-PYRAMID

This diversion consists in "climbing" the number pyramid shown in Fig. 9, by starting with the base number 123456789 (or with the corresponding number at a higher level of the pyramid) and ending with the number 1 at the top of the pyramid, in accordance with the sequence of operations indicated below. The calculations leading to the principle numbers 123... and 987... should be performed as chain operations, and only the principal numbers should be purposely displayed in the course of the calculations.

*Calculation sequence*

123456789 x 8+9=987654321
[(987654321—1)÷10—8]÷8=12345678
12345678 x 8+8=98765432
[(98765432—2)÷10—7]÷8=1234567
1234567 x 8+7=9876543
[(9876543—3)÷10—6]÷8=123456
123456 x 8+6=987654
[(987654—4)÷10—5]÷8=12345
12345 x 8+5=98765
[(98765—5)÷10—4]÷8=1234
1234 x 8+4=9876
[(9876—6)÷10—3]÷8=123
123 x 8+3=987
[(987—7)÷10—2]÷8=12
12 x 8+2=98
[(98—8)÷10—1]÷8=1

*Calculation formula*

123..N x 8+N=987..(10—N)
[[987..(10—N)—(10—N)]÷10—(N—1)]
÷8=123..(N—1)

Two or more persons using identical calculators can "race" to the top of the pyramid to

*FIGURE 9*

*The first number-pyramid. This pyramid shows how to convert a natural sequence of digits into its symmetric counterpart.*

see who is the first to arrive at the last 1. Several persons using the same calculator and a stop watch can race against the clock to see who arrives at the last 1 in the shortest time. A race is always performed as a single chain operation (without intentionally displaying any intermediate results) in order not to waste any time. In the case of the race against each other, any participant may request at any time after the beginning of the race an "inspection stop" by saying the word "stop." When such a request is made, the participants are allowed to press only those keys that are needed to display the current results of their calculations, and then all participants must wait until the inspection is completed before continuing the calculations. If an error is found in the number appearing in the display of somebody's calculator, this person must return to a pyramid level lower than that reached by any other participant at the time of inspection. When a participant reaches the top of the pyramid, he simply says the word "one" announcing his arrival at the final 1 of the pyramid. If desired, the calculators may be inspected at this time in order to determine who has won the second place, etc.

## 5-2. DESCENDING THE FIRST NUMBER-PYRAMID

This diversion consists in "descending" the number pyramid shown in Fig. 9, by starting with the top number 1 and ending with the base number 123456789 (or with the corresponding number at a higher level of the pyramid). As before, the calculations leading to the principal numbers 123... and 987... are performed as chain operations, and only the various principal numbers are intentionally displayed.

*Calculation sequence*

$$(1 \times 8+1) \times 10+8=98$$
$$(98-2) \div 8=12$$
$$(12 \times 8+2) \times 10+7=987$$
$$(987-3) \div 8=123$$
$$(123 \times 8+3) \times 10+6=9876$$
$$(9876-4) \div 8=1234$$
$$(1234 \times 8+4) \times 10+5=98765$$
$$(98765-5) \div 8=12345$$
$$(12345 \times 8+5) \times 10+4=987654$$
$$(987654-6) \div 8=123456$$
$$(123456 \times 8+6) \times 10+3=9876543$$
$$(9876543-7) \div 8=1234567$$
$$(1234567 \times 8+7) \times 10+2=98765432$$
$$(98765432-8) \div 8=12345678$$
$$(12345678 \times 8+8) \times 10+1=987654321$$
$$(987654321-9) \div 8=123456789$$

*Calculation formula*

$$(123..N \times 8+N) \times 10+(9-N)=987..(9-N)$$
$$[987..(9-N)-(N+1)] \div 8=123..(N+1)$$

As in the preceding diversion, several persons with identical calculators can race against each other to the base of the pyramid or, by using the same calculator, can race against the clock to see who arrives at the base in the shortest time. Naturally, all calculations are performed as a single chain operation, to avoid any unnecessary loss of time. Also in this case, when several persons race against each other, any participant may request an inspection stop, as was explained in the preceding diversion. In the case of an error, the person who has made it must return to a level higher than that appearing in the calculator of any other participant. When a participant reaches the base of the pyramid, he announces his arrival there by saying the word "base." If desired, the calculators may then be inspected in order to establish relative positions of the participants at the end of the race.

## 5-3. CLIMBING THE SECOND NUMBER-PYRAMID

This diversion consists in "climbing" the number pyramid shown in Fig. 10, in accordance with the sequence of operations indicated below. Inasmuch as the most important numbers in this pyramid are the principal numbers 987... and 888..., only these numbers should be intentionally displayed in the course of the calculations; the calculations should otherwise be performed as a chain operation.

*FIGURE 10*

*The second number-pyramid. This pyramid shows how to obtain numbers containing only the digit 8.*

As before, several persons with identical calculators can race against each other to the top (the final 9) of the pyramid, or can race against the clock using the same calculator.

*Calculation pattern*

98765432 x 9+0=888888888
[(888888888—8)÷10—1]÷9=9876543
9876543 x 9+1=88888888
[(88888888—8)÷10—2]÷9=987654
987654 x 9+2=8888888
[(8888888—8)÷10—3]÷9=98765
98765 x 9+3=888888
[(888888—8)÷10—4]÷9=9876
9876 x 9+4=88888
[(88888—8)÷10—5]÷9=987
987 x 9+5=8888
[(8888—8)÷10—6]÷9=98
98 x 9+6=888
[(888—8)÷10—7]÷9=9

*Calculation formula*

987..N x 9+(N—2)=8..8 ◀(10—N+1) digits
(10—N+1) digits ▶[(8..8—8)÷10—(N—1)]÷9
=987..(N+1).

## 5-4. DESCENDING THE SECOND NUMBER-PYRAMID

This diversion is identical to Diversion 5-2, except that the pyramid shown in Fig. 10 is used. The calculation pattern and the corresponding formula are shown below. As before, a pyramid race can be performed in accordance with the explanations given above.

*Calculation pattern*

$$9 \times 9+7=88$$
$$(88 \times 10+8-6) \div 9=98$$
$$98 \times 9+6=888$$
$$(888 \times 10+8-5) \div 9=987$$
$$987 \times 9+5=8888$$
$$(8888 \times 10+8-4) \div 9=9876$$
$$9876 \times 9+4=88888$$
$$(88888 \times 10+8-3) \div 9=98765$$
$$98765 \times 9+3=888888$$
$$(888888 \times 10+8-2) \div 9=987654$$
$$987654 \times 9+2=8888888$$
$$(8888888 \times 10+8-1) \div 9=9876543$$
$$9876543 \times 9+1=88888888$$
$$(88888888 \times 10+8-0) \div 9=98765432$$

*Calculation formula*

$$987..N \times 9+(N-2)=8..8 \blacktriangleleft (10-N+1) \text{ digits}$$
$$(10-N+1) \text{ digits} \blacktriangleright [8..8 \times 10+8-(N-3)] \div 9$$
$$=987..(N-1)$$

## 5-5. CLIMBING THE THIRD NUMBER-PYRAMID

This diversion is similar to Diversions 5-1 and 5-3, except that the number pyramid shown in Fig. 11 is used. We would like to point out that this particular pyramid is quite frequently used for designing and performing various "magic tricks" and complex entertainments. Therefore anyone who wants to become an "expert" in performing such tricks should consider memorizing the numerical structure of this pyramid. As before, a pyramid race can be performed in accordance with the explanations given for Diversion 5-1.

*Calculation pattern*

12345678 x 9+9=111111111
[(111111111—9)÷9—8]÷10=1234567
1234567 x 9+8=11111111
[(11111111—8)÷9—7]÷10=123456
123456 x 9+7=1111111
[(1111111—7)÷9—6]÷10=12345
12345 x 9+6=111111
[(111111—6)÷9—5]÷10=1234
1234 x 9+5=11111
[(11111—5)÷9—4]÷10=123
123 x 9+4=1111
[(1111—4)÷9—3]÷10=12
12 x 9+3=111
[(111—3)÷9—2]÷10=1

*Calculation formula*

123..N x 9+(N+1)=1..1◀(N+1) digits
(N+1) digits▶[[1..1—(N+1)]÷9—N]÷10
=123..(N—1)

*FIGURE 11*

*The third number-pyramid. This pyramid shows how one can obtain numbers containing only the digit 1 by multiplication and addition.*

## 5-6. DESCENDING THE THIRD NUMBER-PYRAMID

This diversion is similar to Diversion 5-4, except that the pyramid shown in Fig. 11 is used. As already mentioned in Diversion 5-5, the pyramid shown in Fig. 11 is quite frequently used for performing various "magic tricks" and complex entertainments. Therefore it is desirable to memorize the calculation pattern leading from one to another level of this pyramid.

*Calculation pattern*

$$1 \times 9+2=11$$
$$(11 \times 10+1-3) \div 9=12$$
$$12 \times 9+3=111$$
$$(111 \times 10+1-4) \div 9=123$$
$$123 \times 9+4=1111$$
$$(1111 \times 10+1-5) \div 9=1234$$
$$1234 \times 9+5=11111$$
$$(11111 \times 10+1-6) \div 9=12345$$
$$12345 \times 9+6=111111$$
$$(111111 \times 10+1-7) \div 9=123456$$
$$123456 \times 9+7=1111111$$
$$(1111111 \times 10+1-8) \div 9=1234567$$
$$1234567 \times 9+8=11111111$$
$$(11111111 \times 10+1-9) \div 9=12345678$$

*Calculation formula*

$$123..N \times 9+(N+1)=1..1 \blacktriangleleft (N+1) \text{ digits}$$
$$(N+1) \text{ digits} \blacktriangleright [1..1 \times 10+1-(N+2)] \div 9 = 123..(N+1).$$

*FIGURE 12*

*The fourth number-pyramid. This pyramid shows how to reduce or build up natural sequences of digits and also how to generate numbers containing only the digit 1.*

## 5-7. CLIMBING AND DESCENDING THE FOURTH NUMBER-PYRAMID

This diversion consists in "climbing" or "descending" the number pyramid shown in Fig. 12, in accordance with the calculation pattern reproduced below. As can be seen from Fig. 12, this number pyramid has nine internal "stairs" and "bridges." Each bridge has the property that, if one crosses it from left to right, one arrives at a number equal to the sum of all the numbers located in the left-hand part of the pyramid on the level of the bridge and on the higher levels. For example: crossing the third bridge from the top leads to $123 = 111 + 11 + 1$. Each staircase allows one to go from one level to the next. Also with this pyramid a race to the top or to the base can be performed in accordance with the explanations given for Diversions 5-1 and 5-2.

*Calculation pattern for ascending the pyramid*

$$123456789 - 111111111 = 12345678$$
$$12345678 - 11111111 = 1234567$$
$$1234567 - 1111111 = 123456$$
$$123456 - 111111 = 12345$$
$$12345 - 11111 = 1234$$
$$1234 - 1111 = 123$$
$$123 - 111 = 12$$
$$12 - 11 = 1$$

*Calculation formula*

$$123..N - 1..1 \blacktriangleleft N \text{ digits} \blacktriangleright = 123..(N-1).$$

*Calculation pattern for descending the pyramid*

$$
\begin{aligned}
1 + 11 &= 12 \\
12 + 111 &= 123 \\
123 + 1111 &= 1234 \\
1234 + 11111 &= 12345 \\
12345 + 111111 &= 123456 \\
123456 + 1111111 &= 1234567 \\
1234567 + 11111111 &= 12345678 \\
12345678 + 111111111 &= 123456789
\end{aligned}
$$

*Calculation formula*

$$123..N+1..1 \blacktriangleleft (N+1) \text{ digits} \blacktriangleright = 123..(N+1).$$

## 5-8. BRIDGING THE PYRAMIDS

This diversion consists in performing a series of calculations leading from a certain level (number) of the first number-pyramid to a similar level of the third, then to a similar level of the second pyramid, and, finally, back to the initial level of the first pyramid. The calculation patterns for all eight possible levels are reproduced below.

*Calculation pattern*

$$1 \times 9+2=11; \quad 11 \times 8=88;$$
$$(88-7)\div 9=9; \quad (9-1)\div 8=1$$
$$12 \times 9+3=111; \quad 111 \times 8=888;$$
$$(888-6)\div 9=98; \quad (98-2)\div 8=12$$
$$123 \times 9+4=1..1; \quad 1..1 \times 8=8..8;$$
$$(8888-5)\div 9=987; \quad (987-3)\div 8=123$$
$$1234 \times 9+5=1..1; \quad 1..1 \times 8=8..8;$$
$$(8..8-4)\div 9=9..6; \quad (9..6-4)\div 8=1234$$
$$12345 \times 9+6=1..1; \quad 1..1 \times 8=8..8;$$
$$(8..8-3)\div 9=9..5; \quad (9..5-5)\div 8=12345$$
$$123456 \times 9+7=1..1; \quad 1..1 \times 8=8..8;$$
$$(8..8-2)\div 9=9..4; \quad (9..4-6)\div 8=123456$$
$$1234567 \times 9+8=1..1; \quad 1..1 \times 8=8..8;$$
$$(8..8-1)\div 9=9..3; \quad (9..3-7)\div 8=1234567$$
$$12345678 \times 9+9=1..1; \quad 1..1 \times 8=8..8;$$
$$8..8\div 9=9..2; \quad (9..2-8)\div 8=12345678$$

*Calculation formula*

$$123..N \times 9+(N+1)=1..1 \blacktriangleleft (N+1) \text{ digits}$$
$$(N+1) \text{ digits} \blacktriangleright 1..1 \times 8=8..8$$
$$(N+1) \text{ digits} \blacktriangleright [8..8-[10-(N+2)]]\div 9$$
$$=98..(10-N)$$
$$[98..(10-N)-N]\div 8=12..N$$

## 5-9. FLYING THE NUMERICAL MAGIC CARPET

This diversion consists in displaying, in the course of a chain operation, the various eight-

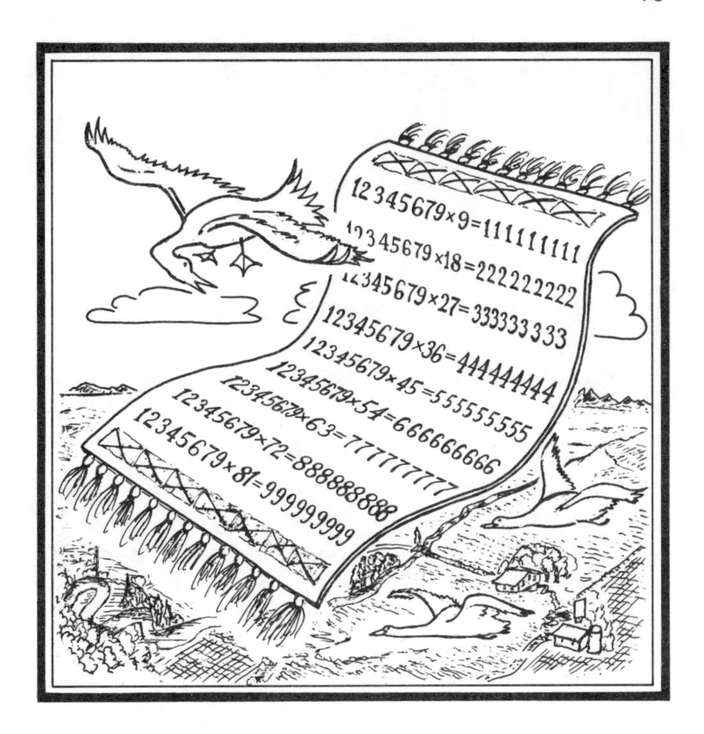


*FIGURE 13*

*The numerical magic carpet. It shows how one can generate 9-digit numbers made up from the same digit.*

and nine-digit numbers shown in the "magic carpet" of Fig. 13. The calculation pattern for this diversion is shown below. A "flying carpet race" can be conducted in the same manner as the pyramid races described above.

*Calculation pattern*

$$12345679 \times 9 \times 1 = 111111111 \div 09 = 12345679$$
$$12345679 \times 9 \times 2 = 222222222 \div 18 = 12345679$$
$$12345679 \times 9 \times 3 = 333333333 \div 27 = 12345679$$
$$12345679 \times 9 \times 4 = 444444444 \div 36 = 12345679$$
$$12345679 \times 9 \times 5 = 555555555 \div 45 = 12345679$$
$$12345679 \times 9 \times 6 = 666666666 \div 54 = 12345679$$
$$12345679 \times 9 \times 7 = 777777777 \div 63 = 12345679$$
$$12345679 \times 9 \times 8 = 888888888 \div 72 = 12345679$$
$$12345679 \times 9 \times 9 = 999999999 \div 81 = 12345679$$

*Calculation formula*

$$12345679 \times 9 \times N = NNNNNNNNN$$
$$NNNNNNNNN \div (9 \times N) = 12345679$$

If your calculator does not handle nine-digit numbers, you can perform the calculation with 0.9, 1.8, 2.7, etc., rather than with 9, 18, 27, etc.; for example, $12345679 \times 0.9 \times 6 = 66666666$. (This number is not exact; the calculator suppresses the remaining decimals. Therefore the next operation, $66666666 \div 5.4$, yields 12345678 instead of 12345679. To correct the error, you will have to add 1 each time after the number 12345678 appears in the calculator).

# 6

# TRICKS THAT ARE NICE, NASTY, AND MEASURED

In this chapter we describe fifteen lighthearted tricks that you may want to present to your guests at a small party. The first five may be called "nice," because they compliment your guests on some imaginary talents, abilities, and the like. The next five may be called "nasty," because they do just the opposite. The last five may be called "measured," because they can do whatever you want them to do. Most of these tricks are based on numerical relations presented in Chapter 5. The tricks can be performed with a calculator of any type, although a calculator with an eight-digit display and a floating decimal point is usually assumed. Some of the tricks may require slight, and usually self-evident, modifications if calculators of other types are used. When such modifications are not self-evident, additional instructions are provided.

## A. NICE TRICKS
*(to make friends)*

### 6-1. HOW TO DEMONSTRATE SOMEONE'S SUPERIOR MATHEMATICAL INTUITION

1. Enter 12345679 in the display of your calculator.
2. Ask your guest to tell you his "favorite" one-digit number.
3. Now say: "Amazing! You have a superior mathematical intuition. Do you know that your favorite number has a most remarkable mathematical property of being able to reproduce itself?"
4. Pass the calculator to your guest and ask him to multiply, in a chain operation, the displayed number by 0.9 and then by his favorite number. To your guest's pleasant surprise, eight windows of the calculator display will light up with his favorite number, "demonstrating" his superior mathematical intuition.

*Example*

Let your guest's favorite number be 6. Performing the multiplications, your guest obtains: $12345679 \times 0.9 \times 6 = 66666666$.

*Trick formula*

$$12345679 \times 0.9 \times N = NNNNNNNN$$

*Note:* Enter 123456.79 if your calculator does not have a floating decimal point.

## 6-2. HOW TO DEMONSTRATE SOMEONE'S OUTSTANDING MATHEMATICAL CREATIVITY

1. Ask your guest to cross out all digits from the sequence 123456789 except the one that he chooses as the "most creative" digit.
2. Enter the chosen digit nine times in the display of your calculator.
3. Now say: "Remarkable! You have a most excellent mathematical creativity. Do you know that the digit that you have chosen is the one from which the entire sequence can be recreated?"
4. Pass the calculator to your guest and ask him to divide, in a chain operation, the displayed number by the chosen digit, then by 0.9, and then to subtract 1. The calculator will show 123456789, thus "demonstrating" your guest's outstanding mathematical creativity.

*Example*

Let the chosen number be 5. Performing the operations yields: $555555555 \div 5 \div 0.9 - 1 = 123456789$.

*Trick formula*

$$\text{NNNNNNNNN} \div \text{N} \div 0.9 - 1 = 123456789$$

*Note:* If your calculator does not accept more than eight digits, tell your guest that the "entire sequence, except for the last digit" can be recreated from the chosen digit, enter the chosen digit only eight times, and omit the subtraction of 1; the calculator will display 12345678 after the two divisions are performed. If your calculator does not have a floating decimal point, enter the decimal point in front of the two last digits (ask your guest to subtract 0.01 rather than 1 in the last step of the calculation if your calculator has a fixed decimal point but accepts nine digits).

## 6-3. HOW TO DEMONSTRATE SOMEONE'S EXQUISITE MATHEMATICAL TASTE

1. Ask your guest to cross out several first consecutive digits in the number 123456789.
2. Enter the remaining digits in their reverse order in the display of your calculator.
3. Now say: "By George! You have an exquisite mathematical taste. Do you know that the figures that you have left untouched are exactly those that will generate one of the most beautiful numbers in existence: a number that does not change when you turn it upside down or reflect it in a mirror?"
4. Pass the calculator to your guest and ask him to multiply, in a chain operation, the dis-

played number by 9 and to add the number of the digits that he has crossed out less one. The figure 8 will light up in several windows of the display (their number is equal to the number of the retained digits plus one), "demonstrating" your guest's exquisite mathematical taste. If the number of 8's appearing in the display is four or less, ask your guest, as the last step of the calculation, to perform a multiplication by 10...01, where the number of digits is one more than the number of the displayed 8's. This will instantly and very effectively double the number of 8's in the display (see Section 1-3).

*Example*

Let us assume that your guest has crossed out the first four digits. You enter the number 98765 in the calculator. Performing the operations, your guest obtains: $98765 \times 9 + 3 = 888888$.

*Trick formula*

98..(N+1) × 9+(N—1)=8..8 ◀ (9—N+1) digits.

*Note:* If your calculator does not have a floating decimal point, you may want to press the decimal point key before entering the last two digits of the number 987..., in which case you will ask your friend to add 0.01, 0.02, etc., instead of 1, 2, etc., (the number of crossed-out digits less one).

## 6-4. HOW TO DEMONSTRATE SOMEONE'S UNIQUE MATHEMATICAL PERCEPTION

1. Ask your guest to cross out two or more last consecutive digits in the number 123456789.
2. Enter the remaining digits in the display of your calculator.
3. Now say: "Most interesting! You definitely have a unique mathematical perception. Do you know that the figures that you have not crossed out are exactly those that will convert themselves into the most economical number that can be obtained with a given number of digits?"
4. Pass the calculator to your guest and ask him to multiply, in a chain operation, the displayed number by 9 and to add the number of the digits that he has retained plus one. The display will show a series of 1's (whose number is one more than the number of the retained digits), thus "demonstrating" your guest's superior mathematical perception.

*Example*

Suppose that your guest crosses out the last four digits. You enter 12345 in the calculator. Performing the operations, your guest obtains: $12345 \times 9 + 6 = 111111$.

*Trick formula*

$$123..N \times 9+(N+1)=1..1 \blacktriangleleft (N+1)\text{digits.}$$

## 6-5. HOW TO DEMONSTRATE SOMEONE'S REMARKABLE MATHEMATICAL IMAGINATION

1. Ask your guest to choose several first consecutive digits in the number 123456789.
2. Enter the chosen digits in their proper order in the display of your calculator.
3. Now say: "I knew it! You have an absolutely remarkable mathematical imagination. Do you know that you have chosen precisely those digits that transform themselves into their symmetric counterparts in the number 123456789?"
4. Pass the calculator to your guest and ask him to multiply, in a chain operation, the displayed number by 8 and to add the number of the chosen digits. The calculator will display the digits 987... (symmetric counterparts of the chosen digits 123...), thus "demonstrating" your guest's remarkable mathematical imagination. (It is interesting to note that if the two symmetric numbers are added and then divided by 10, the result is a series of 1's.)

*Example*

Let the selected digits be 1234. Performing the calculations, your guest obtains: $1234 \times 8 + 4 = 9876$.

*Trick formula*

$$123..N \times 8 + N = 987..(9 - N + 1).$$

## B. NASTY TRICKS
*(to make enemies)*

### 6-6. HOW TO PROVE SOMEONE'S ZERO MATHEMATICAL ABILITY

1. Ask your victim to write down his "favorite" one-digit number without letting you see it.
2. Enter 123456.79 in the display of your calculator.
3. Now shake your head and say: "That's what I thought! It appears that you have no mathematical ability at all. But let us see what kind of rating you will get from the calculator upon a more thorough examination."
4. Pass the calculator to your victim and ask him to multiply the displayed number, without divulging to you the intermediate results, by his favorite number, then by 0.9, then to divide by 10001, then by 101, then by 11, then to multiply by 100, and finally to subtract his favorite number.
5. Then say: "Your mathematical ability rating has been completed, and your exact rating on a scale of 0 to 100 is in the display. I am sure it agrees very closely with my initial evaluation." (Unless your victim has made errors in the calculation, the display will show 0.)

*Example*

Let the favorite number be 7. The operations yield: 123456.79 × 7 × 0.9 ÷ 10001 ÷ 101 ÷

$11 \times 100 - 7 = 0.$

*Trick formula*

$$123456.79 \times N \times 0.9 \div 10001 \div 101 \div 11 \times 100 - N = 0.$$

## 6-7. HOW TO PROVE SOMEONE'S ZERO MATHEMATICAL IMAGINATION

1. Ask your victim to write down his "favorite" one-digit number without letting you see it.

2. Enter any number in your calculator and then clear the calculator (the purpose of this step is to impress your victim with your "magic" powers).

3. Shake your head and say: "Remarkable! As far as I can tell, you have no mathematical imagination whatsoever. But let us see what rating you will get from the calculator on a scale of 0 to 100 after a more complete test."

4. Pass the calculator to your victim and ask him to enter his favorite number seven times in the display, then to enter the decimal point, then to enter two more times his favorite number. Next, ask him to divide the resulting number by 9, then by his favorite number, and then to subtract 123456.79.

5. Now declare: "The test has been completed. The final rating appears in the display (it should be 0.00; see, however, the

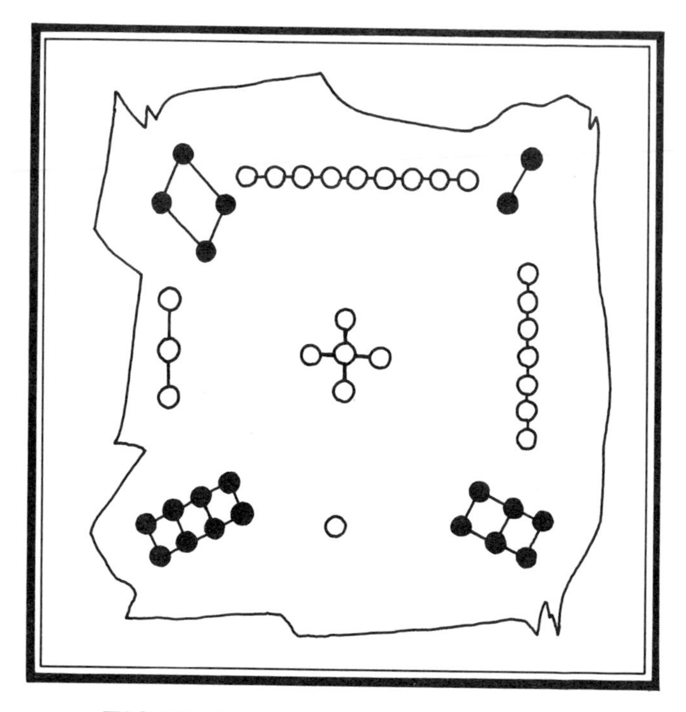

*FIGURE 14*

*This diagram is probably the oldest "magic square" [see Chapter 8] presently known. It appeared in a Chinese book written several thousand years ago. Each group of circles depicts a number equal to the number of the circles. The dark circles represent even, or "feminine," numbers; the light circles represent odd, or "masculine," numbers. In this square the sum of the numbers in each row, column, or diagonal [the "square constant"] is 15.*

note, below). I am sure that it agrees very closely with my initial estimate."

*Example*

Let the favorite number be 8. The operations yield: 8888888.88 ÷ 9 ÷ 8 — 123456.79 = 0.00.

*Trick formula*

$$\text{NNNNNNN.NN} \div 9 \div \text{N} - 123456.79 = 0.00$$

*Note:* If your calculator does not handle nine-digit numbers, the display will show —0.01, in which case you may comment: "I knew that your mathematical imagination was extraordinarily bad, but I did not know that it was even less than zero."

## 6-8. HOW TO PROVE THAT SOMEONE HAS NO MATHEMATICAL TASTE

1. Ask your victim to cross out two or more first consecutive digits in the number 123456789 without letting you see them.
2. Enter any number in the calculator and then clear the calculator (this step serves no purpose except to suggest to your victim that you have some supernatural ability).
3. Shake your head and say: "That's what I suspected all along. It looks as if you have no mathematical taste. But let the calculator give you an exact numerical rating on a scale of 0 to 100 upon a more exhaustive test."

4. Pass the calculator to your victim and ask him to enter in the calculator the digits that he has retained in their reverse order. Then ask him to multiply the number so obtained by 9, then to add the number of digits that he has crossed out less one, then to divide by 8, then to divide by 9, then to divide by one with as many zeros as there are digits that he has retained. Now ask your victim to subtract from the final result all the decimals (suppress the decimals).

5. Announce to your victim that the test has been completed, that the exact numerical rating of his mathematical taste on a scale of 0 to 100 is now displayed in the calculator (it will be 0), and that it should be "in close agreement with my initial evaluation."

*Example*

Let the retained digits be 456789. The calculations produce: $(987654 \times 9 + 2) \div 8 \div 9 \div 1000000 = 0.12...$ ▶ suppress decimals $= 0$.

*Trick formula*

$$[98..N \times 9 + (N - 2)] \div 8 \div 9 \div 10^{10-N} = 0.12... \blacktriangleright \text{suppress decimals} = 0.$$

## 6-9. HOW TO PROVE SOMEONE'S ZERO MATHEMATICAL PERCEPTION

1. Ask your victim to cross out two or more last consecutive digits in the number 123456789

without showing them to you.

2. Enter any number in the calculator and then clear the calculator (this step is a clever adaptation of the time-honored "if-you-cannot-convince-them — confuse-them" technique well known to magicians, college professors, medical doctors, politicians, and other professional people).

3. Now shake your head and say: "Incredible! I am afraid that your mathematical perception is practically zero. But let us see how the calculator will rate you on a 0 to 100 scale upon a more detailed examination."

4. Pass the calculator to your victim and ask him to enter in the calculator in their proper sequence the digits that he has retained. Then ask him to multiply the resulting number by 9, then to add the number of retained digits plus one, then to divide by 9, then to divide by one with as many zeros as the number of retained digits, then to multiply by 100. Next ask the victim to suppress the decimals by subtracting them, then to add 88, and then to subtract 100.

5. You can now declare: "The test has been completed. The rating of your mathematical perception is displayed in the calculator. As you can see for yourself, your mathematical perception is definitely zero."

*Example*

Let the retained figures be 123456. Performing the operations yields: (123456 x 9 + 7)

$\div 9 \div 1000000 \times 100$ ▶ suppress decimals ▶ $+ 88 - 100 = 0.$

*Trick formula*

$[12..N \times 9 + (N + 1)] \div 9 \div 10^N \times 100$ ▶ suppress decimals ▶ $+ 88 - 100 = 0.$

## 6-10. HOW TO PROVE SOMEONE'S ZERO MATHEMATICAL INTUITION

1. Ask your victim to cross out two or more last consecutive digits in the number 123456789 without showing them to you.
2. Enter any number in the calculator and clear the calculator (the purpose of this step was explained in the preceding trick).
3. Shake your head and say: "Unbelievable! Your mathematical intuition is even worse than I thought. In fact, it seems that you don't have any at all. But let us see how the calculator will rate you on a scale of 0 to 100 upon a more sophisticated examination."
4. Pass the calculator to your victim and ask him to enter the retained figures in their proper sequence in the calculator display. Now ask the victim to multiply the number so obtained by 8, then to add the number of retained figures, then to divide by one with as many zeros as the number of retained figures, then to multiply by 100. Next ask him to sup-

press the decimals by subtracting them, to add 2, and to subtract 100.

5. Now you can announce: "The examination is completed. Your rating appears in the display, and, I am afraid, it is an absolute zero!"

*Example*

Let the retained figures be 1234567. The calculations yield: $(1234567 \times 8 + 7) \div 10000000 \times 100$ ▶ suppress decimals ▶ $+ 2 - 100 = 0$.

*Trick formula*

$$(12..N \times 8 + N) \div 10^N \times 100$$
▶ suppress decimals ▶ $+ 2 - 100 = 0$.

## C. MEASURED TRICKS
(*to do what you please*)

This series of tricks deals mostly with "evaluating" someone's abilities, aptitudes, and talents on a numerical scale. We have named these tricks the "Hidden Qualities," or "Hi Q," tricks. You can use them for giving a numerical "rating" of someone's ability to drive, to handle money, to fish, to play games, to cook, to study, to do useful work, to concentrate, to be on time, etc. When performing these tricks, you can specify the particular abilities or talents to be "rated," or you can simply tell your guests that you are performing a "hidden qualities" test, and let them figure out for themselves what it means.

## 6-11. HOW TO DETERMINE SOMEONE'S HI Q

1. Ask your guest to tell you his "favorite" one-digit number (this step is used merely to impress the guest).

2. Now say: "It appears that your Hi Q is ..... percent. But let us see how the calculator will rate you upon a more reliable test."

3. Ask your guest to write down his "favorite" three-digit number without showing it to you, pass your calculator to him, and ask him to enter this number twice in the calculator so that a six-digit number appears in the display.

4. Ask him to divide the number in the display, in a chain operation, by 7, then by the original three-digit number, then by 11, then to add (subtract) the difference between the rating that you have predicted and 13.

5. Now say: "Your Hi Q evaluation has been completed. The rating, in percent, is in the display of the calculator. I am sure it agrees very closely with my initial estimate."

This trick is based on reversing the "stretching" of a three-digit number (see Section 1-3) and on the fact that the number 1001 (which "double-stretches" any three-digit number) can be represented as the product of three factors:

$1001 = 7 \times 11 \times 13$. Therefore a division of the "double-stretched" number by the original three-digit number and by any two of these factors results in the appearance of the third factor (13, in the present case) in the calculator.

*Example*

Let the predicted rating be 50%, and let the favorite number be 375. Entered twice, it becomes 375375. The first three operations yield: $375375 \div 7 \div 375 \div 11 = 13$ (you know this). The difference between 50 and 13 is 37. Therefore you ask your guest to add 37 as the last operation. The final result is 50%, as predicted.

*Trick formula*

Let the favorite number be ABC, and let the three factors of 1001 be K, L, and M, so that

$$1001 = K \times L \times M.$$

The formula is then

$$ABCABC \div K \div ABC \div L = M.$$

## 6-12. ANOTHER WAY TO DETERMINE SOMEONE'S HI Q

1. Ask your guest to write down his two "favorite" one-digit numbers and to show one of them to you.

*FIGURE 15*

*This "magic square" [see Chapter 8] appeared in Albrecht Dürer's engraving "Melancholy" in the year of 1514 [this square originated in India]. The sum of numbers in any row, column, or diagonal of this square is 34.*

2. Look at the number and say: "Your Hi Q percentage appears to be ..... percent. But let us see what rating you will obtain from the calculator upon a more accurate evaluation."

3. Pass the calculator to your guest and ask him to enter his second favorite number in the calculator and then, in a chain operation, to multiply it by 999999, to divide by 91, to subtract from the resulting number the same number but with the places of the first two digits interchanged, to divide by 100, and to add (subtract) the difference between 90 and the rating that you have predicted.

4. Now say: "The test has been completed. The accurate rating of your Hi Q appears in the calculator. I am sure it agrees closely with my prediction."

This trick is based on the fact that 999999 ÷ 91 is equal to the "flip-flop" number 10989 (see Section 1-5), and that the difference of the first two digits in the number representing the product of 10989 and any one-digit number is always 1. Therefore the difference of any such product and the number resulting from exchanging the places of the first two digits in it is always 9000. Division by 100 produces 90.

*Example*

Let the predicted rating be 96%, and let the second favorite number be 6. The operations yield: $6 \times 999999 \div 91 = 65934$ and $(65934 - 56934) \div 100 = 90$. By adding 6, one obtains the predicted result.

*Trick formula*

$$A \times 999999 \div 91 = A(A-1)9BC$$
$$[A(A-1)9BC - (A-1)A9BC] \div 100 = 90.$$

## 6-13. ONE MORE WAY TO DETERMINE SOMEONE'S HI Q

1. Ask your guest to write down his two "favorite" numbers, one smaller than 7, and the other larger than 7. Then ask him to show the larger number to you.
2. Look at the number and say: "There is no doubt in my mind that your Hi Q is ..... percent. However, let us see how the calculator will rate you upon a more exhaustive examination."
3. Ask your guest to enter his smaller "favorite" number in the calculator and, in a chain operation, to multiply it by 9, by 111, by 1001, and to divide by 7. Then ask him to notice the third largest digit in the resulting number, to clear the calculator, to enter the third largest digit in the display, to multiply it by 20, and to subtract the difference between the predicted rating and 100.
4. Now say: "The examination has been completed. Your Hi Q percentage appears in the display. I am sure it is very close to my initial estimate."

This trick is based on the property of the "stubborn digits" number 142857 (see Section 3-1) to retain its digits when multiplied by a number smaller than 7. The number 142857 is introduced indirectly as $9 \times 111 \times 1001 \div 7$. Since the third largest digit in such a product is always 5, the multiplication by 20 produces 100, from which the predicted rating can then be easily obtained. Naturally, since all the digits of the number obtained after the division by 7 are known, one may use other conclusions of this trick in place of the "third largest digit" conclusion.

*Example*

Let the predicted rating be 75%, and let the favorite number be 6. The operations yield: $6 \times 9 \times 111 \times 1001 \div 7 = 857142$ and $5 \times 20 = 100$. The difference between the predicted rating and 100 is 25. Therefore you ask your guest to subtract 25 as the last operation.

*Trick formula*

If N is less than 7, then:

$N \times 9 \times 111 \times 1001 \div 7 =$ transposition of 142857.

## 6-14. OTHER METHODS FOR DETERMINING SOMEONE'S HI Q

Any of the tricks presented in Section B of this chapter ("Nasty Tricks") can be used for obtaining any desired Hi Q rating, since the outcome of the calculations used in these tricks is completely predetermined.

## 6-15. HOW TO DETERMINE HUSBAND'S AND WIFE'S COMPATIBILITY

1. Ask the gentleman and the lady to tell you their "favorite" one-digit numbers.

2. Write down the "compatibility ratings" that you want to give to the gentleman and to the lady. Enter in the calculator the last two digits of the current year, multiply by 2, and subtract the gentleman's rating. Do the same for the lady's rating. Write down the two numbers. Then enter in the calculator the gentleman's favorite number three times.

3. Now say: "It appears that each of you is at least ..... percent compatible. But let us see how the calculator will rate you upon a more intimate examination."

4. Pass the calculator to the gentleman and ask him to add to the number in the display the year of his birth, to subtract his favorite number, to add his age as of the end of the current year, to subtract his favorite number times ten, to add the year of his marriage, to subtract his favorite number times one hundred, to add the number of years that he has been married (as of the end of the current year), to subtract 3800, and to subtract the number that you calculated for him in Step 2.

5. Then say: "Your compatibility rating is now in the display of the calculator. I suspect that it is approximately ..... percent."

6. Ask the lady to take the calculator, to

enter three times her favorite number, to add to it the number of years that she has been married, to subtract her favorite number, to add the year of her marriage, to subtract her favorite number times ten, to add her age, to subtract her favorite number times one hundred, to add the year when she was born, to subtract 3800, and to subtract the number that you calculated for her in Step 2.

7. Then say: "Your compatibility rating is now in the display of the calculator. I believe that it is very close to ..... percent. Congratulations!"

This trick is based on the fact that adding the number representing a year to the number representing the time elapsed since that year results in the number representing the current year. Since two such additions are performed in this trick, the result will be twice the number representing the current year. By subtracting 3800 (which is 2 × 1900), one removes the century numbers from the result and leaves the number formed by the two last digits of the current year times two. By entering the favorite number three times in the calculator, one makes the trick less obvious.

*Example*

Let the gentleman's favorite number be 6, and that of the lady be 7. You decide to give 99% to the gentleman and 100% to the lady. The current year is 1975. You calculate for the gentleman: $75 \times 2 - 99 = 51$. For the lady you calculate: $75 \times 2 - 100 = 50$. Let us assume that the gentleman and the lady were born in 1951 and 1955, respectively, and were married in 1971. The gentleman calculates: $666 + 1951 - 6 + 24 - 60 + 1971 - 600 + 4 - 3800 - 51 = 99$. The lady calculates: $777 + 4 - 7 + 1971 - 70 + 20 - 700 + 1955 - 3800 - 50 = 100$.

*Trick formula*

NNN + year of event — N + years elapsed — (10 × N) + year of event — (100 × N) + years elapsed — (2 × current century) = 2 × (two last digits of the current year).

# 7

# MAGIC TRICKS

The most spectacular numerical tricks that can be performed with the pocket calculator are tricks for finding secret numbers, dates, and places by "mind reading," as well as tricks for communicating secret numbers by means of "telepathy." Tricks of this type originated centuries ago. Many such tricks were described in 17th and 18th century books on magic. The pocket calculator makes these tricks much more entertaining and intriguing, and allows one to perform them more effectively than ever before.

## 7-1. WHICH HAND?

Give one of your guests a nickel and a dime and ask him to hold one coin in his left hand and the other in his right hand without letting you see where the coins are. Now say: "I shall determine the location of the coins through a mental communication with you, which I shall establish with the aid of my calculator." Pass the calculator to him and ask him to multiply the value of the coin in his left hand by any number whose last digit is 6 (or any other even digit), to add the value of the coin in his right hand, and to divide by 2. Then take the calculator and look at the display. If the number in the display has no decimals, the nickel is in the left hand; if it has decimals, it is in the right hand. Announce the location of the coins and ask the guest to open his hands to verify your statement.

*Example*

Your guest holds the dime in his left hand and the nickel in his right. He chooses to multiply by 123456. The calculations yield $(10 \times 123456 + 5) \div 2 = 617282.5$. Since the last number has decimals, you know that the nickel is in the right hand.

*Calculation program*

If $[(\text{left hand coin}) \times .....6 + (\text{right hand coin})] \div 2$ has no decimals, the nickel is in the left hand.

## 7-2. WHERE IS THE RING?

Put a ring on the table and ask one of your guests to place it on his finger, while you are not looking, but so that all other guests can see who takes the ring and on which hand and finger it is placed. Now declare that you will find the ring by using the "method of mental communication." Assign a number to each of your guests, assign a number to each finger (thumb is 1, little finger is 5), and assign number 1 to the left hand and number 2 to the right hand. Then say: "I shall now ask some of you various questions in a mathematical language, so that proper impressions can be formed in the calculator for the purpose of establishing a mental communication between us." Ask one of the guests to enter in the calculator the number identifying the guest who took the ring, to multiply this number by 2, and to pass the calculator to another guest. Ask this guest to add 5, to multiply by 5, and to pass the calculator to the next guest. Ask him to add the number identifying the finger, to multiply by 10, and to pass the calculator to the last guest. Ask this guest to add the number identifying the hand and to subtract 111. Now take the calculator, subtract 139, and say: "The ring is on the ..... finger, of the ..... hand, of my friend ..... ," as you read in the display the three numbers identifying the finger, the hand, and the guest.

*Example*

Let guest No. 5 place the ring on the 3rd finger of his right hand (2). The calculation sequence yields: $[(5 \times 2 + 5) \times 5 + 3] \times 10 + 2 - 111 - 139 = 532$.

*Calculation program*

$[(\text{person} \times 2 + 5) \times 5 + \text{finger}] \times 10 + \text{hand} - 111 - 139 =$ person, finger, hand in the display.

## 7-3. TELL THE NUMBERS THROWN WITH TWO DICE

Let one of your guests throw two dice. Ask him to enter in the calculator the number appearing on the first die, to multiply it by 2, to add 5, to multiply by 5, to add the number appearing on the second die, and to pass the calculator to you. Now subtract 25 and surprise your guests by reading the two numbers from the display.

*Example*

Let the two numbers be 2 and 6. The calculations yield: $(2 \times 2 + 5) \times 5 + 6 - 25 = 26$.

*Calculation program*

Let the two numbers be A and B. Then:

$$(A \times 2 + 5) \times 5 + B - 25 = A,B \text{ in the display.}$$

## 7-4. IDENTIFY TWO CARDS DRAWN FROM A DECK

Ask one of your guests to draw two cards from a deck containing only the aces, 5's, 6's, 7's,

*FIGURE 16*

*One of the numbers in this drawing is definitely wrong. Can you tell which one?*

9's, jacks, queens, and kings. Tell him to count the number cards by their numbers and the face cards as 2, 3, and 4, respectively. Pass to him your calculator and ask him to multiply the number of his first card by 5, to add 7, to multiply by 2, to add the number of the second card, and to pass the calculator to you. Subtract 14 and read the display. The first digit in the display represents the first card, the second digit represents the second card.

*Example*

Let the first card be a queen (3) and let the second be a nine. The calculations yield: $(3 \times 5 + 7) \times 2 + 9 - 14 = 39$.

*Calculation program*

Let the two numbers be A and B. Then:

$$(A \times 5 + 7) \times 2 + B - 14 = A,B \text{ in the display.}$$

## 7-5. IDENTIFY FOUR CARDS DRAWN FROM A DECK

Ask your guests to draw four cards from the deck described in the preceding trick (only three cards should be drawn if your calculator does not handle 10-digit numbers). Tell them to count spades as 1, clubs as 2, diamonds as 3, hearts as 4, and to count the various cards in each suit as before. Ask the first guest to enter the number of his card in the calculator, to multiply it by 2, to add 1, and to multiply by 5. Ask him then to add the number of the suit of his card, to multiply by 2, to add 1, to multiply by 5, and to pass the calculator to the next guest. Ask him to add the number of his card, to multiply by 2, to add 1, etc., and to pass the calculator to the next guest. Continue until all cards and their suits are entered in the calculator. Now take the calculator, subtract 55555555 (555555 for three cards), and divide by 10. The number of each card followed by the number of its suit will appear in the display. Announce the cards to your guests.

*Example*

Let three cards be drawn and let them be 6 of clubs, king of diamonds, and queen of hearts. The calculations produce: $[[(6 \times 2 + 1) \times 5 + 2] \times 2 + 1] \times 5 + 4 \ldots - 555555 \div 10 =$ 624334.

*Calculation program*

Let the card numbers be a,b,c,d and let their suits be A,B,C,D, respectively. Then:

$$[[(a \times 2 + 1) \times 5 + A] \times 2 + 1] \times 5 + b \ \ldots - 55555555 \div 10 = \text{a,A, b,B, c,C, d,D in the display.}$$

## 7-6. IDENTIFY SEVERAL CARDS DRAWN FROM A DECK

Ask your guests to draw several cards (not

exceeding the digit capacity of your calculator less 1) from the deck described in the preceding trick. Ask the first guest to enter the number of his card, to multiply it by 2, to add 1, to multiply by 5, and to pass the calculator to the next guest. Ask him to add the number of his card, to multiply by 2, to add 1, to multiply by 5, and to pass the calculator to the next person, and so on, until all the cards have been entered in the calculator. Then take the calculator, subtract the number 5..5 containing as many digits as the number of drawn cards, and divide by 10. The result will be a number whose digits represent the drawn cards in their order.

*Example*

The following seven cards were drawn: 7, 8, queen (3), king (4), 9, 9, jack (2). The calculations yield: $[[(7 \times 2+1) \times 5+8] \times 2+1] \times 5+3$ ..... $- 5555555 \div 10 = 7834992$.

*Calculation program*

Let the card numbers be a, b, c, d, etc. Then:

$$[[(a \times 2+1) \times 5+b] \times 2+1] \times 5+c \; \ldots - 555\ldots \div 10 = a,b,c \ldots \text{ in the display.}$$

## 7-7. WHAT IS YOUR AGE?

Ask your guest to enter his age in the calculator, to subtract from it his "favorite" one-digit number, to multiply by 9, and to add his age to the product. Then take the calculator and say: "Your age has been impressed in the calculator. Although invisible to anyone else, the impressed numbers are clearly visible to me. Your age is ..... years."

The secret of this trick lies in the fact that the above calculations (for an age of not less than 10 years) always produce a number such that, when its last digit is added to the number formed by the preceding digits, the age is obtained.

*Example*

The age is 27 years, the favorite number is 8. The calculations yield: $(27-8) \times 9 + 27 = 198$. You compute: $19 + 8 = 27$.

*Calculation program*

Let the age be A and let the favorite number be F. Then:

$$(A - F) \times 9 + A = KLM; \quad A = KL + M.$$

## 7-8. WHEN WERE YOU BORN?

Ask one of your guests to enter in the calculator the number of the month when he was born, "so that you can form a mental vision of it." After a second or two of "concentration" ask him to multiply this number by 100. Now tell him that a mental communication between you and him has been established, and ask him, in a chain operation, to add to this product the day of the month when he was born, to multiply by 2, to add 8, to multiply by 5, to add 4, to multiply by 10, to add 4 once again, to add the last two digits of the year when he was born, and, finally, to subtract 3333. Then ask the guest to pass the calculator to you and say: "I have guided you mentally so that you would enter an impression of your date of birth in the display." Add 2889 to the number in the calculator and read the date as follows: the last two digits are the year, the preceding two are the day, the first two (or one) are the month. If the month is a one-digit number, only five digits will appear in the display.

*Example*

The guest was born on October 14, 1922. The numbers for the month, the day, and the year are 10, 14, and 22, respectively. The operations yield: $[[(10 \times 100 + 14) \times 2 + 8] \times 5 + 4] \times 10 + 4 + 22 - 3333 + 2889 = 10\ 14\ 22$.

*Calculation program*

$$[[(\text{month} \times 100 + \text{day}) \times 2 + 8] \times 5 + 4] \times 10 + 4 + \text{year} - 444$$
$$= \text{month, day, year in the display.}$$

## 7-9. FIND THE SECRET WORD

The series of calculations used in the preceding example, or a similar series, can also be used for finding any three numbers having not more than two digits each, such as the day, hour, and minute of an event (airplane departure, lecture, doctor visit, etc.). Furthermore, it can be used to find a set of three numbers in which the first number has any number of digits, while the other two have no more than two digits each (the first number can be the price of an airplane ticket, the second and the third numbers can be the day and hour of departure, etc.).

Here is a very spectacular trick that can be performed by means of such a series of calculations. Give your guests a thick book, ask them to open it on any page, and ask them to memorize some word appearing on this page, noting the number of the line in which the word appears as well as the position number of the word in the line. Then ask your guests to close the book. Now ask each guest to perform one of the calculations in the following series "so that you can establish a mental contact with them:" enter the page number, multiply by 201, add the line number, add 12, subtract the page number, add the line number, multiply by 5, add 5, multiply by 10, add 16, add the word number, subtract 5555. When the calculations are completed, take the calculator, "explain" to your guests that the word is now impressed in the calculator "through their combined mental powers," and add 4889 to the number in the display. Then read in the display the location of the word (the last two digits give the position

| | (1) | (2) | (3) | (4) | (5) | (6) | (7) | (8) | (9) | (10) |
|---|---|---|---|---|---|---|---|---|---|---|
| (1) | **1** | 3 | 5 | 7 | 9 | 11 | | | | |
| (2) | 1 | **4** | 7 | 10 | 13 | 16 | | | | |
| (3) | 1 | 5 | **9** | 13 | 17 | 21 | | | | |
| (4) | 1 | 6 | 11 | **16** | 21 | 26 | | | | |
| (5) | 1 | 7 | 13 | 19 | **25** | 31 | | | | |
| (6) | 1 | 8 | 15 | 22 | 29 | **36** | | | | |
| (7) | | | | | | | | | | |
| (8) | | | | | | | | | | |
| (9) | | | | | | | | | | |
| (10) | | | | | | | | | | |

*FIGURE 17*

*This is an example of a "magic array" of numbers [see Chapter 8]. It has the following remarkable properties: [1] the sum of all the numbers in each right-angled channel is equal to the channel number [circles] multiplied twice by itself; [2] the diagonal numbers [bold face] are equal to the channel number multiplied once by itself; [3] the sum of the numbers in any square array whose diagonal is formed by diagonal numbers [bold face] is equal to a product of a whole number multiplied once by itself [for example, 144 = 12 × 12 for the marked square]. Verify these properties and complete the array.*

in the line, the preceding two give the line, the remaining digits give the page), open the book, find the word, and tell it to your guests.

*Example*

Let the page number, the line number, and the word number be 575, 15, and 2, respectively. The calculations yield: $[(575 \times 201 + 15 + 12 - 575 + 15) \times 5 + 5] \times 10 + 16 + 2 - 5555 + 4889 = 575\ 15\ 02$.

*Calculation program*

[(201 × page+line+12—page+line) × 5+5] × 10 +16+position—666=page,line,position.

## 7-10. FIND THE SECRET HIDING PLACE

Ask your guests to agree among themselves on a secret hiding place identifiable by a house number, floor number (1 to 9; it is a small house), room number (also 1 to 9; the same reason), and drawer number (likewise 1 to 9; how many drawers could there be?). Then say: "I will now show how one uses mental communication for finding secret hiding places."

Pass the calculator to the first guest and ask him to enter the house number in the calculator, to multiply it by 2, to add 5, to multiply by 5, and then to pass the calculator to the second guest. Ask this guest to add 10, to add the floor number, to multiply by 10, then to pass the calculator to the next guest. Ask him to add the room number, to multiply by 10, and to pass the calculator to the next guest. Ask him to add 35, to add the drawer number, and to subtract 1111. Now take the calculator, subtract 2424 and say: "The secret hiding place is located at .....," as you read the house number, the floor number, the room number, and the drawer number from the display of the calculator (the last three numbers are single-digit numbers).

*Example*

Let the four numbers be 137, 8, 6, and 3, respectively. The calculation sequence yields: $[[(137 \times 2 + 5) \times 5 + 10 + 8] \times 10 + 6] \times 10 + 35 + 3 - 1111 - 2424 = 137863$.

*Calculation program*

$$[[(\text{h.n.} \times 2 + 5) \times 5 + 10 + \text{f.n.}] \times 10 + \text{r.n.}] \times 10 + 35 + \text{d.n.} - 1111 - 2424$$
$$= (\text{h.n.})(\text{f.n.})(\text{r.n.})(\text{d.n.}) \text{ in the display.}$$

## 7-11. PREDICTING THE DIFFERENCE OF TWO NUMBERS

Show one of your guests the sequence 987654321 and ask him to enter in the calculator any number formed by several consecutive digits of this sequence without showing it to you. Ask him to tell you how many digits he entered.

After waiting for a few moments, "to establish a mental contact," ask him to subtract from this number the number formed by the same digits taken in their natural sequence. As soon as your guest completes the subtraction, pull from your pocket a sealed envelope containing the number obtained by your guest. Explain that you had guided your guest by "mental communication" to come up with this number in the display of the calculator.

The secret of this trick lies in the fact that the difference of any two numbers formed in accordance with the above prescription is always one of the following numbers

| | | | |
|---|---|---|---|
| 09 | (2) | 198 | (3) |
| 3087 | (4) | 41976 | (5) |
| 530865 | (6) | 6419754 | (7) |
| 75308643 | (8) | 864197532 | (9) |

where the figures in parentheses indicate the number of digits in each of the two numbers used for the subtraction. The above numbers can be easily constructed or memorized (in case you prefer to announce the result without using the envelope) in accordance with the following rules: (a) the first numbers in the two columns are 09 and 198, (b) each number has the same number of digits as the two numbers whose difference it represents, (c) each number is obtainable from the preceding number of the same column by writing the figure representing the number of the digits less 1, followed by the preceding number less 1, and followed by a figure equal to 10 less the first figure.

Before performing the trick, you must prepare eight envelopes containing all eight possible numbers, and either place the envelopes in eight different pockets or use some other means for identifying the envelopes containing the answer with the proper number of digits.

*Example*

Your guest enters 76543, tells you that the number has five digits, and subtracts 34567. By using the above rules, you find that the answer is 41976.

## 7-12. WHAT WAS THE NUMBER?

Ask one of your guests to enter in the calculator his "favorite" two-digit number. Then say: "By using mental communication with several persons in this room, I shall guide these persons toward identifying your number. Please enter your number two more times in the display, so that a six-digit number is obtained, in order to triple the emanations originating from your number. Now divide the number by 3 and pass the calculator to someone else." Ask this guest to divide the number in the calculator by 7 and to pass the calculator to the next person. Ask him to divide by 13 and to pass the calculator to the next person. Ask him to divide by

37 and to read the number in the display. This will be the two-digit number originally entered in the calculator.

The secret of this trick lies in the fact that the product of the four numbers 3, 7, 13, and 37 is 10101. Thus the three divisions are equivalent to a single division by 10101. But this division, when applied to a two-digit number "stretched thrice" (see Section 1-3), restores the number. The trick can be performed with other factors of 10101, such as 21, 13, 37; 7, 39, 37; or 7, 13, 111.

*Example*

Let the favorite number be 75. The operations yield: $757575 \div 3 \div 7 \div 13 \div 37 = 75$.

*Calculation program*

$$\text{ABABAB} \div (\text{factors of } 10101) = \text{AB}).$$

## 7-13. WHERE ARE THE MISSING DIGITS?

Ask one of your guests to enter in the calculator his "favorite" one-digit number, to subtract 3 or 7 (the difference should not be zero), to multiply by 3, 9, 11, 37, and 91 (or by any other numbers whose product is 999999), and to divide by 7. Now say: "I have guided you mentally toward obtaining six different digits in the display. The three digits of the sequence 1 to 9 that are missing are contained in this envelope."

Take out a sealed envelope from your pocket and ask your guest to verify your statement.

The secret of this spectacular trick lies in the fact that the above operations will always produce a transposition of the "stubborn digits" number 142857 (see Section 3-1). The digits in the envelope are always 3, 6, and 9. The subtraction of 3 or 7 from the "favorite" number insures that the number by which the "stubborn digits" number is multiplied is less than 7. The option of using 3 or 7 is given in order to avoid a multiplication by zero when the "favorite" number itself happens to be 3 or 7.

*Example*

Let the favorite number be 1, and let 7 be subtracted from it. The calculations yield: $(1 - 7) \times 3 \times 9 \times 11 \times 37 \times 91 \div 7 = -857142$.

*Calculation program*

Let the favorite one-digit number be F.

$$[F - (3 \text{ or } 7)] \times (\text{factors of } 999999) \div 7 = \text{transposition of } 142857.$$

## 7-14. THE SEALED NUMBER

Write the "flip-flop" number 10989 (see Section 1-5) on a piece of paper, seal it in an envelope, and give it to one of your guests "for safekeeping." Now ask another guest to enter in the calculator his "favorite" one-digit number and say: "Starting with your number, I shall guide you mentally toward obtaining the number in the envelope." Ask him to multiply his number by 3, 9, 11, and 37 (or by any other factors of 10989), to add to the number appearing in the display the same number but with its digits taken in reverse order (the last digit first, the first digit last), and to divide the sum by 10. Then ask him to announce the result, and ask the guest with the envelope to read the sealed number.

The secret of this trick lies in the fact that the above multiplications always produce a five-digit "flip-flop" number, and that the sum of a "flip-flop" number and the reversed number is always ten times the corresponding basic "flip-flop" number (that is, 10890, 109890, etc.). The trick may be modified by sealing in the envelope a "flip-flop" number other than the five-digit one, and other than a basic number. In the former case the multiplication factors must be modified accordingly; in the latter case an appropriate supplementary multiplication must be used.

*Example*

*a.* Let the favorite number be 8. The operations yield: $8 \times 3 \times 9 \times 11 \times 37 = 87912$ and $(87912 + 21978) \div 10 = 10989$.

*b.* You seal the number 65934 (or $10989 \times 6$). Let the favorite number be 4. The operations yield (note the supplementary multiplication by

6): $4 \times 3 \times 9 \times 11 \times 37 = 43956$ and $(43956 + 65934) \div 10 \times 6 = 65934$.

*Calculation program*

Let the sealed number be A × N, where A designates a one-digit number and N designates a basic "flip-flop" number. Let F be the favorite one-digit number. Then:

$$[F \times (\text{factors of N}) + \text{reversed product}] \div 10 \times A = A \times N.$$

## 7-15. THE SEALED NAME

Give one of your guests a sealed envelope containing a name taken from the telephone directory or a word taken from a dictionary. Ask another guest to enter in the calculator his "favorite" three digits. Then say: "Starting with the number formed by your favorite digits I shall guide you mentally toward identifying the name, or word, sealed in the envelope." Ask him to subtract from the number in the calculator the same number read from right to left, then ask him to add to the resulting number (subtract, if the number is negative) that number read from right to left, and then to multiply the sum (difference) by an appropriate number (see below). Now ask him to open the telephone directory (or the dictionary) on the page indicated by the first three (or two) digits of the number appearing in the display, and to read the name or the word whose number from the top or the bottom of the page is represented by the last digit (or two last digits) of the number in the display. Then ask the first guest to open the envelope and to verify the name or the word.

The secret of this fascinating trick lies in the fact that the subtraction and addition just described always result in the basic "flip-flop" number 1089 (see Section 1-5). Knowing this, you seal in the envelope the name or the word located on a line and page represented by this number, or on a line and page represented by the number 1089 multiplied by some one-digit number, in which case a multiplication by that number is added as the last step of the calculations.

*Example*

You decide to use the "flip-flop" number 8712 (or $1089 \times 8$) and a dictionary. You find that the 12th word on the 87th page of your dictionary is "chore." This is the word that you seal in. Suppose that your guest enters the number 385. The calculations yield: $385 - 583 = -198$; $-198 - 891 = -1089$; $-1089 \times 8 = -8712$, which gives the location of the word.

*Calculation program*

$$ABC - CBA = KLM;$$
$$KLM + MLK = 1089 \text{ (or } -1089\text{)};$$
$$1089 \times N = N(N-1)(9-N)(10-N).$$

## 7-16. ADDING THE INVISIBLE NUMBERS

Using construction paper of five different colors, cut out twenty-five differently shaped pieces (five of each color) and write on each of them a number, as shown in Fig. 18a. Turn them over so that the numbers cannot be seen. Ask one of your guests to select five pieces, one of each color, and to place them in front of you. Now say: "I shall use my X-ray vision to read the numbers on these pieces and shall then instantaneously add the five numbers together." After a few moments of "concentration" announce the sum to your guests and ask one of them to verify it by using your calculator.

The secret of this trick lies in the following facts:

(1) The numbers on the similarly shaped pieces have the same last digit — the "code digit."

(2) The sum of the numbers on any five pieces of different colors is always a four-digit number.

(3) The last two digits of this four-digit number form a number equal to the sum of the code digits of the five pieces.

(4) The first two digits and the last two digits of this four-digit number form two numbers whose sum is always 95.

In order to do this trick, you must memorize the code digits associated with the different

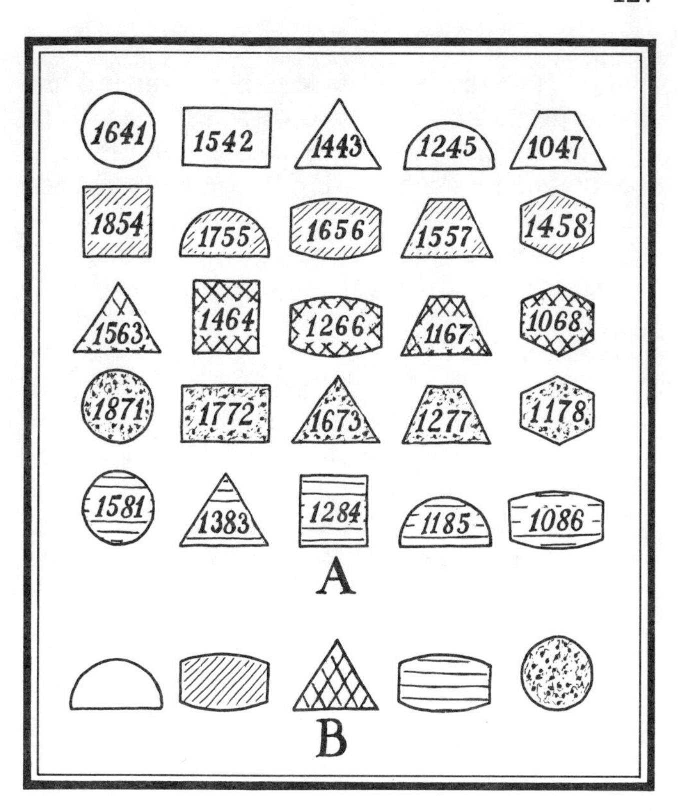


*FIGURE 18*

*Adding the "invisible" numbers is easy once you learn the secret code. The sum of the numbers on the five pieces in [b] is 7421.*

shapes. This will allow you to determine at once the last two digits of the sum by merely adding the code digits of the pieces selected by your guest. The first two digits of the sum are then easily found by subtracting the sum of the code digits from 95. The code digits can be remembered as follows: circle — 1, rectangle — 2, triangle — 3, square — 4; the same shapes distorted correspond to 5, 6, 7, and 8, respectively.

Naturally, instead of asking your guest to select five pieces, you can ask him to select ten (two of each color), etc., in which case the sum of the code digits is subtracted from 190, etc. Also, you can ask several guests to select simultaneously five differently colored pieces each, in which case you will announce the sums of the numbers selected by each guest and will then ask each of them to add his numbers for verification of your statement.

*Example*

Let the five pieces selected by your guest be those shown in Fig. 18b. Their code digits are 5, 6, 3, 6, and 1. Adding them, you find that the last two digits of the sum are: $5 + 6 + 3 + 6 + 1 = 21$. Subtracting this number from 95, you find that the first two digits of the sum are $95 - 21 = 74$. Hence the sum of the numbers on the pieces selected by your guest is 7421.

*Trick formula*

The sum of the numbers on any five pieces of

different colors is ABCD, where AB = (95 − sum of code digits), and CD = (sum of code digits).

## 7-17. TELL THE SUM OF INVISIBLE NUMBERS

Lay out four rows of cards numbered 1 to 28 (see below how to make such cards) and ask your guests to take notice that the 28 numbers are not ordered in any way. Pick up the cards, shuffle them, and place them face down in three rows, nine cards to each row, putting one of the cards (the "extra card") aside. Then say: "I shall now perform one of the greatest magic feats ever attempted. Without using the calculator, and without seeing the card numbers, I shall tell the sum of the numbers on cards of your choice by mentally recording and adding the emanations coming from the cards." Ask your guest to remove a group of three consecutive cards from any row or column, or any combination of such groups, and, if they wish, to remove also the "extra card." After a moment of "deep concentration" announce the sum of the numbers on the removed cards and ask one of the guests to verify your statement with the calculator.

The secret of this fascinating and rather complex trick lies in the following facts:

(1) The 28 cards are initially prearranged

into a deck such that the sequence of the numbers in it is 5 (top card), 7, 28, 20, 3, 12, 14, 16, 22, 27, 21, 23, 25, 18, 11, 8, 1, 6, 2, 13, 17, 10, 15, 4, 9, 26, 19, and 24 (bottom card). The cards are first dealt out and are then collected without destroying this sequence.

(2) The cards are shuffled in a special manner according to the following rule: remove the top three cards from the deck, place the next two on top of the first three, place the next three underneath the first five, place the next two on top, etc., always placing "three underneath and two on top" until all 28 cards have been shuffled. This shuffling arranges the 28 cards in a special sequence, as explained below.

(3) The cards are dealt out face up from the top of the deck so that the first nine cards, in order, form the first of the three rows. The second row is started with the next three cards, but the card that follows is placed aside as the "extra card." The second row is then completed, and the third row is formed.

(4) As a result of the above operations, 27 cards become arranged in the following array

| | | | | | | | | |
|---|---|---|---|---|---|---|---|---|
| 4 | 9 | 2 | 13 | 18 | 11 | 22 | 27 | 20 |
| 3 | 5 | 7 | 12 | 14 | 16 | 21 | 23 | 25 |
| 8 | 1 | 6 | 17 | 10 | 15 | 26 | 19 | 24 |

and the card numbered 28 is the "extra card." This array constitutes three "magic squares" (see Chapter 8) placed side by side. A remarkable property of this array is that the sums of any three consecutive numbers removed from one of its rows are 15, 24, 33, 42, 51, 60, and 69, the first digit of a sum being the "code digit" identifying the column from which the first of the three cards is removed (69 is an exception, since the first digit in it is 6 rather than 7). These sums can be easily memorized by noting that their digits always add up to 6 (69 is again an exception). Another property of this array is that the sum of the numbers in any of its first three columns is 15, the sum of the numbers in any of its three central columns is 42, and the sum of the numbers in any of its last three columns is 69. The "extra card" is always 28. Knowing these properties, you can easily calculate the sum of the numbers on the cards removed by your guests.

*Note:* To make the number-cards, write the numbers 1 to 28 on self-adhesive lables and affix them to 28 playing cards.

*Example*

Your guests remove the second, the third, and the fourth card from the third row and also remove the extra card. Since the first of the three cards was in the second column, the sum of the numbers on the first three cards begins with the digit 2. The second digit is then $6-2=4$, so that the sum is 24. Knowing that the "extra card" is 28, you quickly calculate the sum of all four numbers: $24 + 28 = 52$. Your guests calculate: $5 + 7 + 12 + 28 = 52$.

*Trick formula*

(1) Number sequence in the original deck: 5, 7, 28, 20, 3, 12, 14, 16, 22, 27, 21, 23, 25, 18, 11, 8, 1, 6, 2, 13, 17, 10, 15, 4, 9, 26, 19, and 24.

(2) Shuffle rule: three underneath, two on top.

(3) Sums of three consecutive numbers in any row (see explanation above): 15, 24, 33, 42, 51, 60, 69.

(4) Sum of numbers in the columns of the three subsquares: 15, 42, 69.

(5) Extra card: 28.

# 8

# NUMBER MYSTERIES

In this chapter we describe several "detective" tricks. The first two are based on the so-called "magic arrays." Magic arrays, and "magic squares" in particular, were known in China and India several thousand years ago. They reached Europe in the fifteenth century. Many scientists and philosophers occupied themselves with methods of construction and with properties of magic squares. One of the magic squares constructed by Benjamin Franklin is shown in Fig. 19.

## 8-1. THE STOLEN NUMBERS

Show your guests the array of numbers reproduced in Fig. 20 (or a similar array, see below) and relate the following story: "Several

*FIGURE 19*

*This magic square was constructed by Benjamin Franklin. What is its square constant? This square has many remarkable properties: for example, the four subsquares obtained by cutting it into four equal pieces are also magic. What are its other properties?*

swindlers handling the account of their Company decided to steal some of the Company's money by falsifying the account. The account was in the form of this array of numbers. Since the account was always inspected after one of them handled it, they agreed among themselves to change it in the least noticeable manner, namely as follows: whenever one of them has a chance to put his hands on the account, he removes from it one complete row, column, or diagonal and transfers the corresponding sum to their joint bank account. Furthermore, they agreed that whenever one of them removes less than a complete row, diagonal, or column (which can happen because some of the numbers have already been taken) he must record the missing numbers, so that he will not be accused by the others of stealing these numbers for himself. To their lasting regrets they did not realize how dangerous it is for swindlers to keep any records of their criminal activity. For when a clever detective found the list of the "missing numbers" maintained by the swindlers, he immediately understood their scheme and, without any additional information, determined the amount of money stolen by them from the Company. I shall now show you how the detective did it." Ask each guest to remove numbers of his choice from the array, in accordance with the rules just described, to "deposit the loot in the bank" (calculator) adding all the removed numbers together, and to write down the missing numbers. Then collect the "missing numbers" from each guest, look at the numbers, and announce the total sum that they entered in the calculator.

The secret of this trick lies in the fact that the number array which you give your guests as the "Company account" constitutes a so-called "magic square," in which the sum of the numbers in any row, column, or diagonal is the same: equal to the "square constant." Therefore the total sum entered in the calculator is equal to the square constant multiplied by the number of "swindlers," less the sum of the "missing numbers."

Naturally, the trick may be performed in a "noncriminal" fashion. In this case the guests may play the role of students who are instructed by the host (the "professor") to add the numbers in a row, column, or diagonal of their choice, and to write down the missing numbers, if any. The "professor" collects the "missing numbers" and pronounces the sum, "which he has computed from the missing numbers by means of 'higher mathematics'." Furthermore, the trick can be performed with just one guest, who is asked to remove several rows, columns, or diagonals from the "account."

Magic-square arrays suitable for performing this trick are shown in Figs. 21, 22, and 23. New arrays can be obtained from them by simply adding or subtracting a constant number to or from each number in any of these arrays.

Company Account

| | | | | | |
|---|---|---|---|---|---|
| 1 | 42 | 29 | 7 | 36 | 35 |
| 48 | 9 | 20 | 44 | 13 | 16 |
| 5 | 38 | 33 | 3 | 40 | 31 |
| 43 | 14 | 15 | 49 | 8 | 21 |
| 6 | 37 | 34 | 2 | 41 | 30 |
| 47 | 10 | 19 | 45 | 12 | 17 |

Company Account

| | | | | | |
|---|---|---|---|---|---|
| 1 | 42 | 29 | 7 | 36 | 35 |
| 48 | 9 | 20 | 44 | 13 | 16 |
| 5 | 38 | 33 | 3 | 40 | 31 |
| 43 | 14 | 15 | 49 | 8 | 21 |
| 6 | 37 | 34 | 2 | 41 | 30 |
| 47 | 10 | 19 | 45 | 12 | 17 |

*FIGURE 20*

*The array of numbers in the left-hand part of this drawing is a magic square with the square constant 150. Therefore the sum of all the numbers crossed out from it in the right-hand part of the drawing is simply 150 × [number of crossed out rows, columns, and diagonals] − [sum of numbers at the intersections], or 150 × 4 − [1 + 42 + 9 + 37 + 35] = 476.*

| | | | | | | | |
|---|---|---|---|---|---|---|---|
| 45 | 36 | 29 | 20 | (13) | 4 | 61 | 52 |
| 19 | 30 | 35 | (46) | 51 | 62 | 3 | 14 |
| 44 | 37 | (28) | 21 | 12 | 5 | 60 | 53 |
| 22 | (27) | 38 | 43 | 54 | 59 | 6 | 11 |
| (55) | 58 | 7 | 10 | 23 | 26 | 39 | 42 |
| 9 | 8 | 57 | 56 | 41 | 40 | 25 | (24) |
| 50 | 63 | 2 | 15 | 18 | 31 | (34) | 47 |
| 16 | 1 | 64 | 49 | 48 | (33) | 32 | 17 |

*FIGURE 21*

*This magic square has the square constant 260. Like the square used in Fig. 20, this square is "diabolic," that is, the sum of the numbers taken along any "broken" diagonal [such as the numbers indicated by circles] is also equal to the square constant.*

| 40 | 1 | 2 | 3 | 42 | 41 | 46 |
|---|---|---|---|---|---|---|
| 38 | 31 | 13 | 14 | 32 | 35 | 12 |
| 39 | 30 | 26 | 21 | 28 | 20 | 11 |
| 43 | 33 | 27 | 25 | 23 | 17 | 7 |
| 6 | 16 | 22 | 29 | 24 | 34 | 44 |
| 5 | 15 | 37 | 36 | 18 | 19 | 45 |
| 4 | 49 | 48 | 47 | 8 | 9 | 10 |

*FIGURE 22*

*This 7 × 7 magic square, first constructed in 1544, has the square constant 175. If the boundary squares are discarded, it becomes a 5 × 5 magic square with the square constant 125. The latter square can be similarly transformed into a 3 × 3 square with the constant 75.*

| 100 | 91 | 11 | 12 | 88 | 87 | 15 | 16 | 83 | 2 |
|---|---|---|---|---|---|---|---|---|---|
| 3 | 82 | 23 | 77 | 76 | 26 | 27 | 73 | 20 | 98 |
| 4 | 21 | 68 | 63 | 39 | 40 | 59 | 34 | 80 | 97 |
| 96 | 22 | 35 | 58 | 45 | 44 | 55 | 66 | 79 | 5 |
| 95 | 29 | 36 | 47 | 52 | 53 | 50 | 65 | 72 | 6 |
| 7 | 30 | 37 | 51 | 48 | 49 | 54 | 64 | 71 | 94 |
| 8 | 70 | 60 | 46 | 57 | 56 | 43 | 41 | 31 | 93 |
| 9 | 69 | 67 | 38 | 62 | 61 | 42 | 33 | 32 | 92 |
| 84 | 81 | 78 | 24 | 25 | 75 | 74 | 28 | 19 | 17 |
| 99 | 10 | 90 | 89 | 13 | 14 | 86 | 85 | 18 | 1 |

*FIGURE 23*

*The square constant of this magic square, taken from an 18th century book on magic, is 505.*

*Example*

Consider the array of numbers shown in Fig. 20. The constant of this array is 150. Let one of the guests take the first line, the second guest — the second column, the third guest — the ascending diagonal, the fourth guest — the descending diagonal. The "missing numbers" are 42, 37, 35, 1, and 9. Their sum is 124. Hence the sum of the removed numbers is $4 \times 150 - 124 = 600 - 124 = 476$.

## 8-2. EMBEZZLERS AND THE AUDITOR

This amusing trick can be performed with one or with several guests. One of the guests, the "president," receives a sheet of paper with a group of numbers arranged in several columns and several rows representing the "Company account." The guest "embezzles" one of the numbers by entering it in the calculator. To cover up his "crime" he crosses out the row and the column that contain the embezzled number. Then he passes the calculator and the "account" to the next guest, the "vice-president," who also "embezzles" one of the remaining numbers and adds it to the first number in the calculator; he, too, covers up his "crime" by crossing out the corresponding row and column. Other guests (the "treasurer," the "secretary," etc.) "embezzle" in their turn certain numbers and cross out the corresponding rows and columns until only one number, "the balance," is left on the sheet. The sheet is then passed to you — the "auditor." Taking a look at the remaining number you immediately declare the total amount of the "embezzlement" (the sum of all the "embezzled" numbers as it appears in the display of the calculator, which is still in the possession of the last guest) and ask the last guest to pass the calculator around so that everyone can verify your statement.

The secret of this trick lies in the special arrangement of the numbers given to the guests. To prepare this arrangement, you must first decide on a certain maximum number which will represent the maximum possible sum of the "embezzlement." Let this sum be 1000, for example. Next, you select several arbitrary numbers (two for each "embezzler" and two for yourself) such that their sum is equal to 1000 (or whatever number you had chosen as the maximum). Let the numbers be 1, 30, 70, 135, 171 and 10, 63, 90, 180, and 250. These numbers are then arranged as shown in Fig. 24, one half of the numbers forming the left-hand vertical column, the other half forming the top horizontal row. Now, each number of the vertical column is added in turn to each number of the horizontal row, and the sum of each pair of numbers is written down at the intersection of the horizontal and vertical lines corresponding to each pair. It is these sums that you present (without changing their relative positions) to

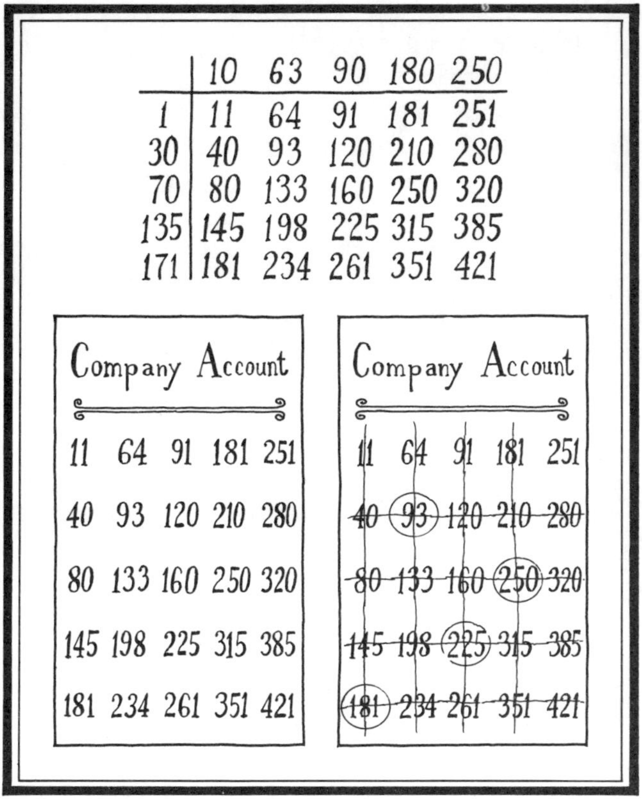

| | 10 | 63 | 90 | 180 | 250 |
|---|---|---|---|---|---|
| 1 | 11 | 64 | 91 | 181 | 251 |
| 30 | 40 | 93 | 120 | 210 | 280 |
| 70 | 80 | 133 | 160 | 250 | 320 |
| 135 | 145 | 198 | 225 | 315 | 385 |
| 171 | 181 | 234 | 261 | 351 | 421 |

Company Account

| | | | | |
|---|---|---|---|---|
| 11 | 64 | 91 | 181 | 251 |
| 40 | 93 | 120 | 210 | 280 |
| 80 | 133 | 160 | 250 | 320 |
| 145 | 198 | 225 | 315 | 385 |
| 181 | 234 | 261 | 351 | 421 |

Company Account

| | | | | |
|---|---|---|---|---|
| 11 | 64 | 91 | 181 | 251 |
| 40 | 93 | 120 | 210 | 280 |
| 80 | 133 | 160 | 250 | 320 |
| 145 | 198 | 225 | 315 | 385 |
| 181 | 234 | 261 | 351 | 421 |

*FIGURE 24*

*When all the numbers but one are crossed out from this array [bottom, left] by vertical and horizontal lines [bottom, right], the sum of the numbers at any four intersections belonging to different rows and columns [such as those shown by circles] is 1000 minus the remaining number.*

your guests as the "Company account." A remarkable property of such an array of numbers is that when any of them are removed in accordance with the procedure explained above, the sum of the removed numbers is always equal to the initial number (1000 in our example) less the last remaining number.

Naturally, the trick can be performed with only one guest, who is asked to add the various numbers and to cross out the corresponding rows and columns until only one number remains on the sheet.

*Example*

Let the "embezzled numbers" be (Fig. 24) 250, 93, 181, and 225. The remaining number is 251. Hence the total "embezzlement" is 1000 − 251 = 749.

## 8-3. THE SECRET PRODUCT

This trick is analogous to the one described in Section 8-1, except that the *products* of the numbers appearing in a row, column, or main diagonal of one of the number arrays shown in Figs. 25 and 26 are entered in the calculator by each guest, who also writes down the "missing numbers." The last guest writes down the "secret" overall product, and clears the calculator. The host collects the "missing numbers" and, using the calculator, finds the "secret"

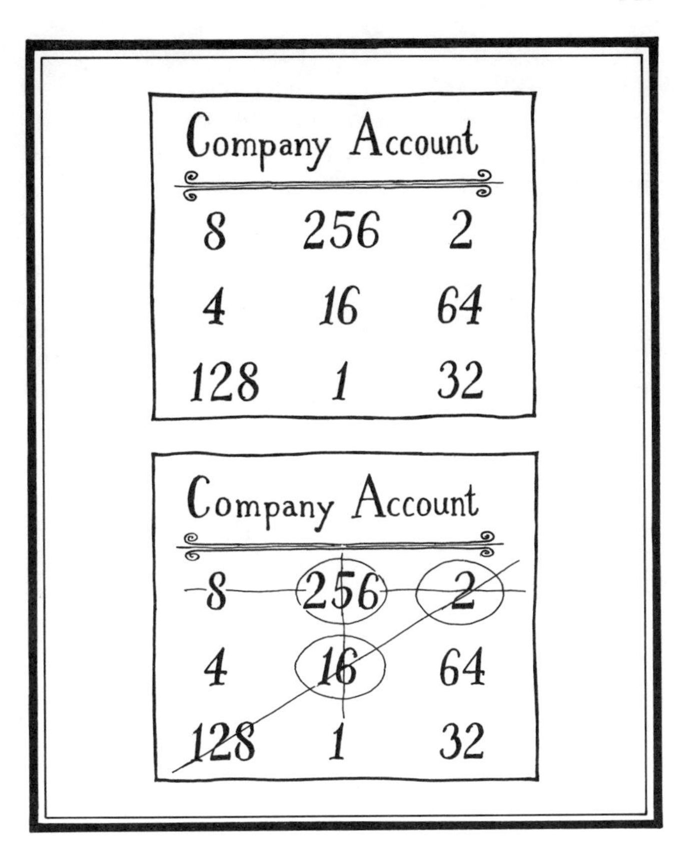


*FIGURE 25*

*The number array shown here constitutes a "product magic square." Its constant is 4096.*

product as a demonstration of his "higher mathematical skills."

This trick is based on the fact that the number array given to the guests is a special kind of magic square: the product magic square. The product of the numbers in any row, column, or diagonal of such a square is a constant. The "secret" product is therefore equal to this constant multiplied by itself as many times as there are participating guests and divided by each "missing number." The trick can be performed very effectively with only one guest, who is asked to multiply the numbers in as many rows, columns, or diagonals as he wishes and then to tell the host the "missing numbers."

New arrays suitable for performing this trick can be produced from those shown in Figs. 25 and 26 by multiplying each number by a constant.

*Example*

Let the numbers be those shown in Fig. 25; the product constant is 4096. Let the first guest remove the first line, the second guest — the midle column, the third guest — the ascending diagonal. The missing numbers are 256, 16, and 2. The guests calculate: 8 × 256 × 2 × 16 × 1 × 128 = 8388608. The host calculates: 4096 ÷ 256 ÷ 16 ÷ 2 × 4096 × 4096 = 8388608 (he performs the division first, in order not to overload the calculator).

*FIGURE 26*

*The arrays shown here are product magic squares with the square constants 19683* [*top*] *and 64* [*bottom*].

## 8-4. THE TREASURY AGENT AND THE SWISS BANKER

Designate four of your guests as the "Swiss banker," the "bank teller," the "inspector," and the "mailman." You are the "treasury agent" who wants to find the number of a secret bank account from the "Swiss banker" with the aid of the "bank teller," the "inspector," and the "mailman."

Ask the "Swiss banker" to write down any number not exceeding six digits (this is the "secret account" number), to enter it in the calculator, and to pass the calculator to the "bank teller". Ask him to multiply this number by 2, to add 4, and to pass the calculator to the "inspector." Ask him to multiply by 5, to add 12, and to pass the calculator to the "mailman." Ask him to multiply by 10, to subtract 320, and to pass the calculator to you. Now divide by 100 and read the secret number in the display. Ask the "Swiss banker" to confirm the number.

*Example*

Let the secret number be 639865. The calculations yield: $[[(639865 \times 2+4) \times 5+12] \times 10-320] \div 100=639865$.

*Calculation program*

$$[[(Z \times 2 + 4) \times 5 + 12] \times 10 - 320] \div 100 = Z.$$

## 8-5. THE TAXPAYER AND THE TAX COLLECTOR

Tell your guests that you will demonstrate a "secret mathematical method" used by tax collectors and undercover investigators for determining the income that dishonest taxpayers do not report on their tax returns.

Ask one of your guests to be the "taxpayer" and ask another guest to be the "investigator." Ask the "taxpayer" to write down the income that he did not report and to enter it in the calculator, rounding off the amount to the nearest dollar. Then ask him to multiply this amount by 3 and to divide by 2. Now ask if the result is a whole number or a fraction. If it is a whole number, ask him to pass the calculator to the "investigator." If it is a fraction, ask him to add 0.5 and then to pass it to the "investigator." Ask the "investigator" to multiply by 3, to divide by 9, to suppress the decimals in the final result (if any) by subtracting them, and to pass the calculator to you — the "tax collector." Multiply the last number by 2 and, if you instructed the "taxpayer" to add 0.5, add 1. The result is the unreported income. Announce it to the "taxpayer" for verification.

*Example*

Let the number entered in the calculator be 5437. The calculations yield: $5437 \times 3 \div 2 =$

8155.5; $(8155.5 + 0.5) \times 3 \div 9 = 2718.66...$; $(2718.66... - 0.66...) \times 2 + 1 = 5437$.

*Calculation program*

$$Z \times 3 \div 2(+0.5) \times 3 \div 9 \ (-\text{decimals}) \times 2(+1) = Z,$$

where the expressions in parentheses indicate additional operations that must be performed when the intermediate results appear with fractions.

## 8-6. THE DETECTIVE AND THE TWO CONSPIRATORS

Give your guests identification numbers 1 to 9 (you can use playing cards for this purpose) and request that two of them, with consecutive identification numbers, become "conspirators" for the purpose of this demonstration of your skills as a "number detective." Explain that the "conspirators" and their identification numbers should be known to the rest of the guests, but not to you. Leave the room to allow the guests to choose the two "conspirators." Upon returning, pass the calculator to one of the guests and ask him to enter the identification number of the first "conspirator," to multiply it by the identification number of the second "conspirator," and then to pass the calculator to another guest. Ask this guest to subtract the smaller of the two identification numbers, to multiply by this number, and to pass the calculator to the next guest. Ask this guest to multiply by 1001, to subtract 110, and to pass the calculator to you. Identify the two "conspirators" by using the following rule: if the last digit in the calculator display is

1,2,3,4,5,6,7,8, or 9,

the smaller of the two identification numbers is

1,8,7,4,5,6,3,2, and 9,

respectively, (since the two "conspirators" have consecutive identification numbers, the larger number is the smaller number plus 1).

*Example*

Let the identification numbers of the two conspirators be 5 and 4. The calculations yield: $(5 \times 4 - 4) \times 4 \times 1001 - 110 = 63954$. Since the last digit is 4, the two numbers, according to the above rule, are 4 and 5.

*Calculation program*

Let the smaller number be N. We have

$$[(N + 1) \times N - N] \times N \times 1001 - 110 = .....Y,$$

where Y is the last digit, from which N can be found in accordance with the above mentioned rule or by computing in your mind the $N \times N \times N$ product that ends with Y.

# 9 CHEERFUL HODGEPODGE

In this chapter we describe several cheerful arithmetical tricks built around imaginary stories involving familiar and universally admired heroes from the world of literature. The heroes appear to be doing very strange things. But look at the results! No matter how strange their methods may be, they always get the correct numbers and solve their problems without fail.

## 9-1. ALI BABA SAVES PRINCESS SHAHRAZAD

Relate the following story to your guests: "The forty thieves decided to kidnap Princess Shahrazad and her 143 servants from her 533-

*FIGURE 27*

*Ali Baba calculates. Can he save Princess Shahrazad from the forty thieves?*

room palace on one of the 1001 nights, but not later than on the 999th night and, preferably, not on the 7th or 13th night, because of prior commitments. Ali Baba learned about the plot from his 11 brothers, who were hiding in the cave, and, by using his mathematical skills, saved the Princess. I shall now demonstrate how he did it."

Ask one of the guests ("leader of the 40 thieves") to write down the number identifying the night of the intended kidnapping, to enter this number in the calculator, and to pass the calculator to the next guest ("one of the 40 thieves"). Ask this guest to multiply the number by the "1001 nights," and to pass the calculator to the next guest. Ask this guest to divide by the "7th night," to subtract the "143 servants," and to pass the calculator to the next guest. Ask this guest to divide by the "11 brothers," to add the "533 rooms," and to pass the calculator to the next guest. Ask this guest to divide by the "13th night," to subtract the "40 thieves" and to pass the calculator to you. Take the calculator, press the "=" key, and say, as you read the number in the display: "Ali Baba looked at the result of this calculation and recognized that the final number was that of the night for which the attack on the palace was planned, namely the ..... night. He immediately communicated his discovery to the Princess. And that is how the Princess was saved." Ask the first guest to verify the number.

*Example*

Let the attack be planned for the 832nd night. The calculations yield: $[(832 \times 1001 \div 7 - 143) \div 11 + 533] \div 13 - 40 = 832$.

*Calculation program*

$$[(N \times 1001 \div 7 - 143) \div 11 + 533] \div 13 - 40 = N.$$

## 9-2. LONG JOHN SILVER FINDS PIRATE TREASURE

Relate the following story to your guests: "Long John Silver knew that a party of 20 pirates (only 3 of whom returned to the ship) had buried a treasure consisting of 5 boxes, each containing 222 gold coins, 100 diamonds, and 111 silver coins. He also knew that the treasure was buried at 6 bells and that, to find the treasure, one had to count less than 100 steps due north, starting from the big tree, then less than 100 steps due west, then less than 100 steps due south. But only the 3 pirates knew the exact number of steps. I shall now demonstrate to you how Long John, by using certain mathematical operations, found out the exact location of the treasure."

Ask three of your guests ("3 pirates") to write down the three step counts (any three numbers from 1 to 99) without showing the numbers to you. Then pass the calculator to the

*FIGURE 28*

*Long John Silver works out a mathematical program for finding the treasure.*

first guest, ask him to enter in it the number of steps due north, to multiply this number by the "20 pirates," to add the "222 gold coins," to multiply by the "5 boxes," and to pass the calculator to the second guest. Ask him to add the number of steps due west, to multiply by the "100 diamonds," and to pass the calculator to the third guest. Ask him to add the number of steps due south, to add the "111 silver coins," to subtract the "6 bells" in the form of the number 111111, and then to pass the calculator to you. Now take the calculator, press the "=" key, and say, as you read the number in the display: "And that is exactly how Long John Silver found the location of the treasure. The number of steps due north, west, and south was ....., ....., and ....., respectively; the very same numbers appearing now in the display of my calculator." Ask your guests to verify the numbers.

*Example*

Let the step counts be 22, 8, and 63. The calculations yield: $[(22 \times 20 + 222) \times 5 + 8] \times 100 + 63 + 111 - 111111 = 220863$.

*Calculation program*

$$[(\text{No} \times 20 + 222) \times 5 + \text{We}] \times 100 + \text{So} + 111 - 111111 = \text{No,We,So}$$

in six windows of the display.

## 9-3. ROBIN HOOD SAVES FRIAR TUCK

Relate the following story to your guests: "Friar Tuck was taken prisoner by the evil Prince John, who locked him up in one of the sixteen dungeons (known as No. 0, No. 1, No. 2, etc.) in the Nottingham Castle. To free Friar Tuck, Robin Hood had to know the exact number of the dungeon. Since nobody was allowed to leave the castle, this information could be obtained only through secret signals from a friendly lady who lived in one of the castle's towers. Therefore Robin Hood sent the following message to the lady: "Dear Lady, please signal to me on the next four nights. On the first night add 1 to the number of the dungeon, multiply by 3, and divide by 2. If the result is a whole number, place one candle in your window. If the result is a fraction, add 0.5 and place two candles in the window. On the second night multiply the last number by 3 and divide by 2. If the result is a whole number, place one candle in the window. If the result is a fraction, add 0.5 and place two candles. Do the same on the third night. On the fourth night divide the last number by 2 and put one or two candles in the window, as before." Although the lady did not understand how Robin Hood could possibly find the number of the dungeon from her candles, she did exactly as he requested. On the fifth night Robin Hood came to the dungeon where Friar Tuck was held and saved him from the terrible

*FIGURE 29*

*Robin Hood looks at the candles in the friendly lady's window. Will he be able to save Friar Tuck?*

fate planned for him by the evil Prince John. I shall now show how Robin Hood found the number of the dungeon by looking at the friendly lady's window."

Pass the calculator to one of your guests and ask him to write a number from 0 to 15 (the "dungeon number"), to enter this number in the calculator, to add 1, to multiply by 3, and to divide by 2. Ask him to say "one candle" if the result is a whole number, and to say "two candles" if the result is a fraction, in which case he should add 0.5 to the result. Now ask him to pass the calculator to the second guest, who should multiply the last number by 3 and divide by 2, saying "one candle" or "two candles" exactly as the first guest did. Ask the third guest to do the same. Finally, ask the fourth guest to divide by 2 and to say "one candle" if the result is a whole number or "two candles" if the result is a fraction. Now consult the table below and then announce to your guests the "dungeon number," which you determined without asking them any questions and without looking at the calculator. (To keep a record of the candle sequence, you can lay out deuces and aces in front of you as the number of candles is announced.)

*Candle sequence*

The possible candle sequences and the corresponding secret numbers ("dungeon numbers") are as follows:

| | |
|---|---|
| 1,1,1,1 — 15 | 1,1,1,2 — 7 |
| 1,1,2,1 — 3 | 1,1,2,2 — 11 |
| 1,2,1,2 — 5 | 1,2,2,1 — 1 |
| 1,2,2,2 — 9 | 2,1,1,1 — 4 |
| 2,1,1,2 — 12 | 2,1,2,1 — 8 |
| 2,1,2,2 — 0 | 2,2,1,1 — 2 |
| 2,2,1,2 — 10 | 2,2,2,1 — 6 |
| 2,2,2,2 — 14 | 1,2,1,1 — 13 |

*Example*

Let the number be 9. The first guest calculates $(9 + 1) \times 3 \div 2 = 15$ and says "one candle." The second guest calculates $15 \times 3 \div 2 = 22.5 + 0.5 = 23$ and says "two candles." The third guest calculates $23 \times 3 \div 2 = 34.5 + 0.5 = 35$ and says "two candles." The fourth guest calculates $35 \div 2 = 17.5 + 0.5$ and says "two candles." According to the table, this sequence of candles (1,2,2,2) corresponds to the dungeon number 9.

*Calculation program*

(1) $(N + 1) \times 3 \div 2$ (+ 0.5 if fraction) $= K$
(2) $K \times 3 \div 2$ (+ 0.5 if fraction) $= L$
(3) $L \times 3 \div 2$ (+ 0.5 if fraction) $= M$
(4) $M \div 2 = Q$

If K,L,M, or Q is a whole number, "one candle" is announced; if a fraction, "two candles" are announced. Use the table to find the secret number.

## 9-4. THE THREE MUSKETEERS AND THE QUEEN'S JEWELS

Relate the following story to your guests: "The three musketeers, Athos, Porthos, and Aramis (also known as No. 1, No. 2, and No. 3), were on a secret mission for the queen: to take her famous jewels — the ring, the braclet, and the necklace — to the three trusted ladies-in-waiting for safekeeping. Just after they delivered the jewels, they were arrested by the cardinal's men and were placed in the Bastille. Soon afterwards the queen needed her jewels and asked D'Artagnan (who was not imprisoned) to retrieve them. D'Artagnan knew to which lady-in-waiting each musketeer delivered a jewel, but he did not know which particular jewel it was. And in accordance with a prior agreement, the ladies would not give the jewels to anyone unless each was asked for the right jewel. To make matters worse, the cardinal forbade the imprisoned musketeers to send messages to the outside, although he allowed them to receive provisions and letters from their friends. Having assessed the situation, D'Artagnan, who always had a remarkable mathematical aptitude, immediately sent to the three musketeers 18 bottles of wine accompanied by the message: "The one with the ring drink as many bottles as his number; the one with the bracelet drink twice as many bottles as his number; the one with the necklace drink four times as many

*FIGURE 30*

*The three musketeers in the Bastille. Each must drink an exact number of bottles, or the queen of France will be in terrible danger.*

bottles as his number." The next day he asked the jailer how many bottles of wine there were left and, by using this information, promptly retrieved the jewels and thus saved the queen's honor. I shall now show how he did it."

Give the numbers 1, 2, and 3 to three of your guests (you can use playing cards for this purpose) and ask each of them to take one of the previously prepared cards with the words "ring," "bracelet," and "necklace," without letting you know who takes what. Now enter 18 in the calculator, pass the calculator to them, ask that the one who has the "ring" subtracts his number from the calculator, the one who has the "bracelet" — twice his number, and the one who has the "necklace" — four times his number. Ask the last guest to pass the calculator to you. Compare the number in display with the table given below and announce who has the "ring," who has the "bracelet," and who has the "necklace."

*Distribution table*

With the abbreviation r, b, and n for "ring," "bracelet," and "necklace" the various final numbers in the display of the calculator signify the following distribution of items among guests No. 1, No. 2, and No. 3, respectively:

| | |
|---|---|
| 1 — r, b, n | 5 — b, n, r |
| 2 — b, r, n | 6 — n, r, b |
| 3 — r, n, b | 7 — n, b, r |

*Example*

Let guest No. 1 have the "bracelet," No. 2 — the "ring," No. 3 — the "necklace." The numbers they subtract are 1 × 2, 2 × 1, and 3 × 4, respectively. Thus the number remaining in the calculator is 18 — 2 — 2 — 12 = 2. According to the above table, the distribution of the items is then b, r, n, which is the actual distribution.

*Calculation program*

Display 18. If the guest's number is N, he subtracts N × 1 for the ring, N × 2 for the bracelet, N × 4 for the necklace. Use the distribution table to find who has each item.

## 9-5. SNOW WHITE AND THE SEVEN DWARFS

Relate the following story to your guests: "Three of the seven dwarfs, No. 4, No. 5, and No. 6, always liked to have ice cream for dessert. The remaining four did not like ice cream: sometimes they wanted apple pie, and sometimes they wanted banana cake. Since it took Snow White a long time to prepare the dessert, she had to know each dwarf's choice for the day long before they returned home from their work in the woods. And since the dwarfs went to work very early, when Snow White was still fast asleep, she could not inquire of their choice in the mornings. Therefore, each evening, Snow

White put 45 peanuts on the dinner table, and, the next morning, when the dwarfs were leaving for work, each dwarf who wanted ice cream or apple pie on that day took as many peanuts as was his number, while each dwarf who wanted banana cake took twice as many peanuts as was his number and then one additional peanut. Later in the day, when Snow White was ready to cook the dinner, she counted the peanuts left on the table and thus learned what each dwarf wanted for his dessert, while in the meantime the dwarfs could eat their peanuts for breakfast and lunch. I shall now present to you a mathematical demonstration of Snow White's method for identifying each dwarf's choice."

Give your guests identification numbers 1, 2, 3, 4, 5, 6, and 7 (you can use playing cards for this purpose). Then give them four cards with the words "apple pie," four cards with the words "banana cake," and three cards with the words "ice cream." Ask the guests whose numbers are 4, 5, and 6 to take the "ice cream" cards, and ask the other four guests to take a card of their choice from the "apple pie" and "banana cake" cards, without letting you see which cards they take. Now enter 45 (the "45 peanuts") in the calculator, pass it to your guests, and ask that each guest who has an "ice cream" or an "apple pie" card subtracts his number from the calculator, while each guest who has a "banana cake" card subtracts twice his number plus 1. Ask the last guest to pass the calculator to you. Take the cal-

*FIGURE 31*

*The seven dwarfs on their way to work. What will Snow White give them for dinner when they return home?*

culator, read the number in the display (it represents the number of peanuts left), and, with the help of the table below, tell each guest what particular "dessert card" he has.

*Distribution table*

(A stands for "apple pie," B stands for "banana cake"). The possible numbers in the display and the corresponding choices of dwarfs No. 1, 2, 3, and 7, respectively, are:

| | |
|---|---|
| 0 — B, B, B, B | 9 — A, A, A, B |
| 2 — A, B, B, B | 10 — A, B, B, A |
| 3 — B, A, B, B | 11 — B, A, B, A |
| 4 — B, B, A, B | 12 — B, B, A, A |
| 5 — A, A, B, B | 13 — A, A, B, A |
| 6 — A, B, A, B | 14 — A, B, A, A |
| 7 — B, A, A, B | 16 — B, A, A, A |
| 8 — B, B, B, A | 17 — A, A, A, A |

*Example*

Let guests No. 1, 2, 3, and 7 have, respectively, "apple pie," "apple pie," "banana cake," and "apple pie." The seven guests subtract the following numbers: $45 - 1 - 2 - (2 \times 3 + 1) - 4 - 5 - 6 - 7 = 13$. From the table you find that the number 13 in the display corresponds to the distribution assumed in the example.

*Calculation program*

Enter 45. If the guest's number is N, he subtracts N for "apple pie" or "ice cream" and $2N + 1$ for "banana cake." Use the distribution table to find the choices.

## 9-6. SHERLOCK HOLMES AND THE SECRET MESSAGE

Relate the following story to your guests: "A secret message was sent by a dangerous criminal to one of his accomplices, who, in turn, sent it to another accomplice for safekeeping. Scotland Yard found out that the message consisted of a five-digit number but could not identify the sender, the addressee, or the person to whom the message was forwarded. As was usual in such difficult cases, they asked Sherlock Holmes to solve the mystery. Without losing any time, Sherlock Holmes opened the Classified Advertisement section of the Times, and soon found there the following message:

Number × + × + + First × + + Second × + + Third

Mr. Sherlock Holm~~e~~s:

Good-looking accomplice became absolutely green.

P.S. Subtract 8765.

He immediately recognized that the message was from an anonymous helper and that it constituted an important clue by means of which the mystery could be solved. With the remarkable insight characteristic of him, he promptly counted the letters in each word of the message and obtained the following numbers: 2 (Mr.), 8 (Sherlock), 5 (Holm~~e~~s, "e" is left out); 47 (good-looking), 10 (accomplice), 6 (became), 10 (absolutely), 5 (green). Next he combined these numbers with the arithmetical symbols preceding the message and subtracted 8765. As a result, he obtained a calculation program which he used later in the day to crack the case, that is, to find the secret number and to identify the three criminals. I shall now demonstrate to you the essence of this program."

Give your guests identification numbers 1 to 9 (use playing cards if you wish). Ask one of the guests to write a five-digit number, to show this number to the rest of the guests and to pass it, without your knowledge, to another guest, who will initial the number and will then pass it to a third guest, who will keep it. Now declare that you shall proceed with the questioning of "witnesses and suspects." Pass the calculator to one of the guests, ask him to enter the secret number in the calculator, to multiply the number by 2, to add 8, to multiply by 5, and then to pass the calculator to another guest. Ask this guest to add 47, to add the number of the guest who wrote the secret number, to multiply by 10, and to pass the calculator to another guest. Ask this guest to add 6, to add the number of the guest who initially received the secret number, to multiply by 10, and to pass the calculator to another guest. Ask this guest to add 5, to add the number of the guest who has the secret message, to subtract 8765, and to pass the calculator to you. Now read the display and say: "The case is solved! The secret number is (the first 5 digits of the display), the sender is (6th digit), the addressee is (7th digit), and the number is now in the possession of (8th digit)."

*Example*

Let the secret number be 36215, the sender be No. 4, the addressee be No. 5, and let the secret number be in the possession of No. 2. The above sequence of calculations yields:

$$[[(36215 \times 2 + 8) \times 5 + 47 + 4] \times 10 + 6 + 5] \times 10 + 5 + 2 - 8765 = 36215452.$$

*Calculation program*

Let the secret number be N, and let the numbers identifying the three guests be A, B, and C. Then:

$$[[(N \times 2 + 8) \times 5 + 47 + A] \times 10 + 6 + B] \times 10 + 5 + C - 8765 = \text{NABC in the display.}$$

## 9-7. THE SECRET WEAPON OF AGENT 007

Relate the following story to your guests: "It is not commonly known that the most important secret weapon of Agent 007, also known as James Bond, was a computer program, which, in order that he would never forget it, consisted of operations corresponding to numerical relations contained in his name and in his identification number. These operations were based on the number 545607, the first four digits of which are

5 (the number of letters in "James"), 4 (the number of letters in "Bond"), 5 (the number of letters in "Agent"), and 6 (the number of letters in "double"); the remaining digits are 07. The first two steps of the program were always the same: the subtraction of the number 545607 from the same number in reverse (that is, from 706545) and the addition of the difference to the difference in reverse. The remaining steps depended on the particular situation to which the program was applied. Let me demonstrate to you this program as applied to ....." (see below).

If you perform the operations constituting the first two steps of the "James Bond" program, you will find that the result is the number 999999 in the display. Consequently, you can use this program for performing any tricks for which this number can be used as the starting point. Among such tricks are those described in Sections 1-5, 2-8, 3-1, 3-6, 6-12, 6-13, 7-13, and 7-14. Select one of these tricks and conclude the above story accordingly.

*Example*

You decide to make use of the "James Bond" program for performing the "Sealed Number" trick described in Section 7-14. Let the number be 65934 (or 10989 × 6). You ask your guest to perform the following operations: 706545 — 545607 = 160938; 160938 + 839061 = 999999. Now ask your guest to divide the number in the display by 91, to multiply by his "favorite" one-digit number (suppose it is 7), to add the product in reverse, to multiply by 6, and to divide by 10. The result is: $999999 \div 91 \times 7 = 76923$; $(76923 + 32967) \times 6 \div 10 = 65934$.

*Calculation program* [*initial steps*]

$$706545 - 545607 = 160938;$$
$$160938 + 839061 = 999999.$$

# 10 MAGICIAN'S TREASURE CHEST

There exist many peculiar, unexpected, and astonishing relations between numbers. It is quite interesting to observe and explore such relations with the aid of the pocket calculator. Moreover, for anyone who wants to develop and perform original arithmetical entertainments and tricks, these types of relations can serve as the foundation upon which the entertainments and tricks can be built. In this chapter we present a collection of such relations.

## 10-1. SOME PROPERTIES OF 37

$37 \times 3 \times 1 = 111$ $37 \times 3 \times 5 = 555$
$37 \times 3 \times 2 = 222$ $37 \times 3 \times 6 = 666$
$37 \times 3 \times 3 = 333$ $37 \times 3 \times 7 = 777$
$37 \times 3 \times 4 = 444$ $37 \times 3 \times 8 = 888$
$37 \times 3 \times 9 = 999$

## 10-2. SOME PROPERTIES OF 77

$77 \times 13 \times 1 = 1001$ $77 \times 13 \times 5 = 5005$
$77 \times 13 \times 2 = 2002$ $77 \times 13 \times 6 = 6006$
$77 \times 13 \times 3 = 3003$ $77 \times 13 \times 7 = 7007$
$77 \times 13 \times 4 = 4004$ $77 \times 13 \times 8 = 8008$
$77 \times 13 \times 9 = 9009$

## 10-3. SOME PROPERTIES OF 91

$91 \times 11 \times 1 = 1001$ $91 \times 11 \times 5 = 5005$
$91 \times 11 \times 2 = 2002$ $91 \times 11 \times 6 = 6006$
$91 \times 11 \times 3 = 3003$ $91 \times 11 \times 7 = 7007$
$91 \times 11 \times 4 = 4004$ $91 \times 11 \times 8 = 8008$
$91 \times 11 \times 9 = 9009$

## 10-4. SOME PROPERTIES OF 99

$99 \times 11 \times 1 = 1089$ $99 \times 11 \times 5 = 5445$
$99 \times 11 \times 2 = 2178$ $99 \times 11 \times 6 = 6534$
$99 \times 11 \times 3 = 3267$ $99 \times 11 \times 7 = 7623$
$99 \times 11 \times 4 = 4356$ $99 \times 11 \times 8 = 8712$
$99 \times 11 \times 9 = 9801$

Observe that in these products the first digit is the same as the last multiplier, the second digit is the first minus 1, the sum of the 1st and 3rd digits is 9, and the sum of the 2nd and 4th digits is also 9 (see also the "flip-flop" numbers, Sections 1-5 and 2-8).

## 10-5. SOME PROPERTIES OF 143

$143 \times 7 \times 1 = 1001$ $\quad$ $143 \times 7 \times 5 = 5005$
$143 \times 7 \times 2 = 2002$ $\quad$ $143 \times 7 \times 6 = 6006$
$143 \times 7 \times 3 = 3003$ $\quad$ $143 \times 7 \times 7 = 7007$
$143 \times 7 \times 4 = 4004$ $\quad$ $143 \times 7 \times 8 = 8008$
$143 \times 7 \times 9 = 9009$

## 10-6. SOME PROPERTIES OF THE "CALENDAR" NUMBER 365

$$365 = 10 \times 10 + 11 \times 11 + 12 \times 12$$
$$365 = 13 \times 13 + 14 \times 14$$
$$(10 \times 10 + 11 \times 11 + 12 \times 12 + 13 \times 13 + 14 \times 14) \div 365 = 2$$

## 10-7. SOME PROPERTIES OF 999999

$999999 \div 91 = 10989$ ("flip-flop" number)
$999999 \div 7 = 142857$ ("stubborn digits" number)

## 10-8. HOW TO GENERATE PALINDROMIC NUMBERS

A palindromic number is a number which does not change when read from left to right. The following examples show how such numbers can be built

$11 \times 11 = 121 \qquad 111 \times 111 = 12321$
$1111 \times 1111 = 1234321$, etc.

$$22 \times 22 \div 2 \div 2 = 121$$
$$33 \times 33 \div 3 \div 3 = 121$$
$$222 \times 222 \div 2 \div 2 = 12321$$
$$333 \times 333 \div 3 \div 3 = 12321$$

## 10-9. INTERESTING WAYS FOR OBTAINING 1

$42 \div 24 \times 12 \div 21 = 1 \quad 63 \div 36 \times 24 \div 42 = 1$
$63 \div 36 \times 12 \div 21 = 1 \quad 84 \div 48 \times 24 \div 42 = 1$
$84 \div 48 \times 12 \div 21 = 1 \quad 84 \div 48 \times 36 \div 63 = 1$
$46 \div 64 \times 96 \div 69 = 1$

$$(11 + 110) \div 11 \div 110 \times 10 = 1$$
$$(14 + 35) \div 14 \div 35 \times 10 = 1$$
$$(15 + 30) \div 15 \div 30 \times 10 = 1$$
$$(20 + 20) \div 20 \div 20 \times 10 = 1$$
$$(12 + 60) \div 12 \div 60 \times 10 = 1$$

## 10-10. MULTIPLICATION WITH SURPRISES

$91 \times 91 = 8281 \qquad 727 \times 727 = 528529$
$428 \times 428 = 183184 \quad 7810 \times 7810 = 60996100$
$573 \times 573 = 328329 \quad 9079 \times 9079 = 82428241$
$9901 \times 9901 = 98029801$

$12 \times 99 = 1188 \qquad 123 \times 999 = 122877$
$1234 \times 9999 = 12338766$, etc.

$2 \times 2 = 4$
$32 \times 32 = 1024$
$332 \times 332 = 110224$
$3332 \times 3332 = 11102224$

$3 \times 3 = 9$
$33 \times 33 = 1089$
$333 \times 333 = 110889$
$3333 \times 3333 = 11108889$

$4 \times 4 = 16$
$34 \times 34 = 1156$
$334 \times 334 = 111556$
$3334 \times 3334 = 11115556$

$5 \times 5 = 25$
$35 \times 35 = 1225$
$335 \times 335 = 112225$
$3335 \times 3335 = 11122225$

$5 \times 5 = 25$
$65 \times 65 = 4225$
$665 \times 665 = 442225$
$6665 \times 6665 = 44422225$

$6 \times 6 = 36$
$66 \times 66 = 4356$
$666 \times 666 = 443556$
$6666 \times 6666 = 44435556$

$6 \times 6 = 36$
$96 \times 96 = 9216$
$996 \times 996 = 992016$
$9996 \times 9996 = 99920016$

$7 \times 7 = 49$
$67 \times 67 = 4489$
$667 \times 667 = 444889$
$6667 \times 6667 = 44448889$

$7 \times 7 = 49$
$97 \times 97 = 9409$
$997 \times 997 = 994009$
$9997 \times 9997 = 99940009$

$8 \times 8 = 64$
$68 \times 68 = 4624$
$668 \times 668 = 446224$
$6668 \times 6668 = 44462224$

$8 \times 8 = 64$
$98 \times 98 = 9604$
$998 \times 998 = 996004$
$9998 \times 9998 = 99960004$

$9 \times 9 = 81$
$99 \times 99 = 9801$
$999 \times 999 = 998001$
$9999 \times 9999 = 99980001$

## 10-11. DIFFERENT WAYS OF "NUMBER STRETCHING"

See Sections 1-1, 1-2, and 1-3.

## 10-12. HOW TO OBTAIN 101, 1001, ETC.

$$78 + 23 = 101$$
$$778 + 223 = 1001$$
$$7778 + 2223 = 10001$$
$$77778 + 22223 = 100001$$
$$777778 + 222223 = 1000001$$
$$7777778 + 2222223 = 10000001$$

$$7 \times 143 = 1001 \qquad 13 \times 77 = 1001$$
$$11 \times 91 = 1001 \qquad 73 \times 137 = 10001$$

$$3 \times 91 \times 37 = 10101 = 7 \times 39 \times 37$$
$$3 \times 13 \times 259 = 10101 = 13 \times 21 \times 37$$
$$3 \times 7 \times 13 \times 37 = 10101 = 7 \times 13 \times 111$$

## 10-13. HOW TO OBTAIN NUMBERS CONTAINING ONLY THE DIGIT 1

$$3 \times 37 = 111 \qquad 41 \times 271 = 11111$$
$$11 \times 101 = 1111 \qquad 33 \times 3367 = 111111$$

$$3 \times 37037 = 111111 = 13 \times 8547$$
$$7 \times 15873 = 111111 = 21 \times 5291$$
$$111 \times 1001 = 111111 = 33 \times 3367$$
$$11 \times 10101 = 111111 = 37 \times 3003$$

$$3 \times 11 \times 91 \times 37 = 111111 = 7 \times 11 \times 39 \times 37$$
$$3 \times 11 \times 13 \times 259 = 111111 = 11 \times 13 \times 21 \times 37$$
$$3 \times 7 \times 11 \times 13 \times 37 = 111111 = 7 \times 11 \times 13 \times 111$$

$$1111 \times 10001 = 11111111 = 11 \times 1010101$$
$$399 \times 333667 = 11111111 = 1507 \times 7373$$

## 10-14. SOME USEFUL WAYS FOR OBTAINING POWERS OF 10

Here are some examples of obtaining powers (repeated products) of ten by multiplication of two numbers. The numbers that are multiplied are repeated products of 2 and 5 (each is multiplied by itself as many times as there are zeros in the corresponding power of 10, less 1).

$$10 = 2 \times 5 \qquad 10000 = 16 \times 625$$
$$100 = 4 \times 25 \qquad 100000 = 32 \times 3125$$
$$1000 = 8 \times 125 \qquad 1000000 = 64 \times 15625$$
$$10000000 = 128 \times 78125$$

## 10-15. FANCY NUMBERS

Throughout this book we have been designating numbers with peculiar properties by unusual names. Among such numbers are the "flip-flop" numbers (Section 1-5), "self-mending" numbers (Section 1-6), and "stubborn-digits" numbers (Section 3-1). Here we give three more examples of such "fancy" numbers.

### A. "Self-Inverting" Numbers

$$2178 \times 4 = 8712 \qquad 1089 \times 9 = 9801$$
$$21978 \times 4 = 87912 \qquad 10989 \times 9 = 98901$$
$$219978 \times 4 = 879912 \qquad 109989 \times 9 = 989901$$
$$2199978 \times 4 = 8799912 \qquad 1099989 \times 9 = 9899901$$

## B. "Dipole" Numbers

$$2244 = 11 \times 204$$
$$222444 = 111 \times 2004$$
$$33334444 = 1111 \times 30004$$
$$3333344444 = 11111 \times 300004$$

## C. "Inseparable" Numbers

$$88209 = (88 + 209) \times (88 + 209)$$
$$494209 = (494 + 209) \times (494 + 209)$$
$$998001 = (998 + 001) \times (998 + 001)$$
$$7441984 = (744 + 1984) \times (744 + 1984)$$
$$4941729 = (494 + 1729) \times (494 + 1729)$$
$$52881984 = (5288 + 1984) \times (5288 + 1984)$$
$$60481729 = (6048 + 1729) \times (6048 + 1729)$$
$$25502500 = (2550 + 2500) \times (2550 + 2500)$$
$$24502500 = (2450 + 2500) \times (2450 + 2500)$$

## D. "Talking" Numbers

B(8): 338, 638, 36138, 7738, 37738, 818, 618, 37818, 7718, 55378, 55178, 8078, 808, 31608, 7108, 5508. E(3): 883, 663, 773, 3573. G(6): 336, 35336, 616, 376616, 7716, 3376, 38076, 55076, 0.6, 378806, 376606, 0.06, 35006, 4506. H(4): 34, 7334, 7734, 0.7734, 14, 4614, 7714, 5514, 514, 378804, 0.804, 304, 604, 3704, 3504. I(1): 0.0761, 771, 51, 3751. L(7), 637, 3781637, 0.37, 5537, 73817, 317, 807, 607, 35007, 3507, 5507. O(0): 35380, 361780, 3080, 553580, 3760, 40, 710, 6370. S(5): 335, 7735, 345, 77345, 3045, 0.045, 4615, 7715, 0.715, 8075, 45075, 805, 505, 3705.

# APPENDIX

To avoid embarrassing mistakes, you should plan your entertainment program ahead of time. Write down an outline of the program and the trick formulas in the upper half of a sheet of paper. Reserve the lower half for making notes and calculations. A sample outline is shown in Fig. 32. It consists of eight entertainments: (1) flip-flop numbers (Section 1-5); (2) 109..989 multiplication (Section 2-8); (3) 142857 multiplication (Section 3-6); (4) Hi Q determination (Section 6-12); (5) finding the date of birth (Section 7-8); (6) adding invisible numbers (Section 7-16); (7) embezzlers trick (Section 8-2); (8) Robin Hood trick (Section 9-3). The time needed for presenting these entertainments is approximately 40 minutes.

Try to present the various tricks in as dramatic a manner as possible. For example, for the Robin Hood trick you can place on the table sixteen numbered cards ("dungeons") and a smaller card with the inscription "Friar Tuck." Ask your guests to place secretly from you the latter card underneath one of the "dungeon" cards. Provide the "friendly lady" with real candles and with a cardboard window. When you know where the "Friar Tuck" card is located, withdraw it from underneath the "dungeon" card and show it to your guests. Try to dramatize other tricks in a similar manner.

1. *Flip-Flop Numbers:* $A(A-1)9..\ 9(9-A)(10-A)$.
2. $109..989 \times$ and $\div$ :
   $109..989 \times A = A(A-1)9..9(9-A)(10-A)$,
   $A(A-1)9..9(9-A)(10-A) \times B \div A = B(B-1)9..9(9-B)(10-B)$.
3. $142857 \times 2,3,4,5,6$, or $7 = ...4, ...1, ...8$, *etc.*
4. *Hi Q:* $A \times 999999 \div 91 = A(A-1)9BC$,
   $[A(A-1)9BC - (A-1)A9BC] \div 100 = 90$.
5. *Date of Birth:* $[[(mo \times 100 + da) \times 2 + 8] \times 5 + 4]$
   $\times 10 + 4 + yr - 3333 + 2889 = mo, da, yr$.
6. *Invisible Numbers:* $ABCD$; $AB = 95 -$ s. of c.d.,
   $CD =$ s. of c.d.
7. *Embezzlers:* $X = 1000 - N$.
8. *Robin Hood:* (1) $(N+1) \times 3 \div 2\ (+0.5) = K$;
   (2) $K \times 3 \div 2\ (+0.5) = L$; (3) $L \times 3 \div 2\ (+0.5) = M$;
   (4) $M \div 2 = Q$; W.N. ~ 1c ; Fr ~ 2c ;
   1111 ~ 15 ; 1121 ~ 3 ; 1212 ~ 5 ; 1222 ~ 9;
   2112 ~ 12 ; 2122 ~ 0; 2212 ~ 10 ; 2222 ~ 14;
   1112 ~ 7 ; 1122 ~ 11; 1221 ~ 1 ; 2111 ~ 4 ;
   2121 ~ 8 ; 2211 ~ 2; 2221 ~ 6 ; 1211 ~ 13.

*Notes:*

*FIGURE 32*

*A sample outline for an entertainment program of 30 to 40 minutes.*

# BIBLIOGRAPHY

## A. Early Books


1. Funk, C. B.: *Natürliche Magie*, Friedrich Nicolai, Berlin and Stettin, 1783.
2. Guyot, M.: *Nouvelles Recreations Physiques et Mathematiques*, Gueffier, Paris, 1786.


## B. Contemporary Books


1. Domoryad, A. P.: *Mathematical Games and Pastimes*, MacMillan, New York, 1964.
2. Gardner, M.: *New Mathematical Diversions from Scientific American*, Simon and Schuster, New York, 1966.
3. Greenblatt, M. H.: *Mathematical Entertainments*, Thomas Y. Crowell, New York, 1965.
4. Hunter, J. A. H. and Madachy, J. S.: *Mathematical Diversions*, D. Van Nostrand, New York, 1963.

5. Kordemsky, B. A.: *The Moscow Puzzles*, Charles Scribner's Sons, New York, 1972.
6. Kraitchik, M.: *Mathematical Recreations*, Dover, New York, 1942.
7. Madachy, J. S.: *Mathematics on Vacations*, Schribner, New York, 1966.
8. Perelman, Y.: *Figures for Fun*, FLPH, Moscow, 1957.
9. Schuh, F.: *The Master Book of Mathematical Recreations*, Dover, New York, 1968.
10. Thebault, V.: *Les Recreations Mathematiques*, Gauthier-Villars, Paris, 1952.

## C. Definitive Book

Ball, W. W. R.: *Mathematical Recreations and Essays*. This is one of the most comprehensive works on mathematical recreations ever written. It was originally published in 1892 and was continually revised by its author through the 10th edition, which was published some thirty years later. At least two modernized editions have been issued since then.

# INDEX

This book was set in Century Textbook.
The format was designed by the author.
The drawings were done by
Dr. D. K. Walker from the author's sketches.
The printer and binder was
Morgantown Printing & Binding Company.